CW00393651

Having Babies

Women's Experiences of Giving Birth

HAVING BABIES

Women's Experiences of Giving Birth

Paddy O'Brien

First published in Great Britain in 1994
Sheldon Press, SPCK, Marylebone Road, London NW1 4DU

British Library Cataloguing-in-Publication Data
A catalogue record for this book is available from the British Library

ISBN 0-85969-698-7

Photoset by Deltatype Ltd, Ellesmere Port, Cheshire
Printed in Great Britain by Biddles Ltd, Guildford and King's Lynn

Contents

To JRM with love

Acknowledgements

My deepest thanks to the women who wrote these birth stories. They put their experiences down in writing to record them in all their uniqueness, and to share them with other women approaching birth, who want to know what it is truly like. Their vivid words and generosity of spirit are the core of the book.

I would also like to thank Marion Symes for her comments on technical matters and her willingness over all these years to discuss birth from every aspect.

The support of Arjan Shahani and Sarah Roch were indispensable to the generation of many of these stories.

Names and identifying details have been changed in these birth stories, but my own are not disguised amongst them. Nevertheless I would like to thank my husband Tim and my children Jon, Ben, Daniel, Zoe and Susanna, for all their love and support.

| *Introduction*

This is a book of birth stories written by women.

The stories are vivid and moving. Most are written within hours, or at most, days of the birth. They are neither censored nor angled, and do not promote or denigrate any particular birthing style.

The stories are important because any woman approaching birth needs access to other women's stories. The details of sensation, emotion, and medical practice are endlessly fascinating.

Many, but not all of them, are birth reports written by women who attended antenatal yoga classes which I ran for many years in an NHS hospital. At these classes we prepared physically and emotionally for childbirth. An important part of this preparation was hearing from women, first-hand, how their deliveries went.

It always seemed important to me that we heard these experiences neat, undiluted – whether triumphant, miserable, or, more often, a confounding mixture of the two. I did not want to tidy anyone up to fit any theories.

I know that by preparing for birth, one can make the most of whatever experience of birth one is destined to have. That preparation needs to be physical, mental, emotional, and spiritual.

This book contributes to your preparation in all those areas. At the end of the book you will find simple stretching and breathing exercises – which are the same as the ones mentioned and followed by many of the women in the stories. The stories also provide a wealth of help for the mental preparation. And, lastly, by sharing each of these births we are able to grow emotionally and spiritually, and understand more about the complex nature of this most fundamental of natural acts.

The sequence of events in childbirth goes like this: during the first stage of labour, the cervix (the entrance to the womb, closed throughout pregnancy) dilates (opens up) by means of regular muscular contractions, to an opening 10 cm in diameter. Once the cervix is fully opened to 10 cm the second stage of labour is said to begin. Great expulsive contractions, which the woman assists by pushing voluntarily as well, push the baby into the vagina, then out into the world. The third stage of labour is complete when the placenta, which has nourished the baby during pregnancy, detaches from the wall of the womb and is also delivered out through the vagina.

The last hour or so of the first stage of labour – 7½–10 cm of dilation, are usually the hardest. This period is known as 'transition' (i.e. the transition from first to second stage), and is usually accompanied by a marked mood change.

For every woman who is expecting a baby, there is a moment of truth at some point during the pregnancy when she realizes *she* is going to have to get her baby out. This can be a lonely moment. My hope is that by making all these stories available it can be less lonely and that the great wealth of women's experience will help. Having read it, you may find it easier to imagine yourself and your baby coming through the birth and meeting each other, safe and well, for the first time.

1
Drug-free Births in the Hospital Setting

Controversy and debate about the place of birth continue. This chapter consists of birth stories from women who had their babies in hospital but had no need of any drugs. They used steady breathing, and followed their instincts, moving into whatever physical position helped them cope with the pain best.

Let us begin with Jenny, at home. This is her second baby who, she is starting to feel, is in no hurry to arrive.

JENNY

'I declare my baby a son'

Baby three days late

06.00 Visit loo, and there's a 'show'*. Yippie at last baby must be coming soon!

12.30 Amanda drops in for lunch, I'm sitting there chatting but really preoccupied with my abdomen – is it contractions or bowel movements? The answer is bowels. Still, could be another sign. Whatever, ignore contractions while I can and thereby save energy for the tough bits.

14.00 Resigned to the fact I've been having the usual Braxton Hicks** with no pattern. I go in to town and then to Safeways.

15.30 Leave Safeways. Not aware of anything except the very occasional twinge. Go to the seafront and eat an apple doughnut with Susie (my two-year-old).

16.10 After a few rather strong contractions, I decide to skip a turn on the swings and feel that perhaps we should go home.

16.20 Phone Pete (husband). Contractions every five minutes now

* Thick jelly-like mucus discharge (often streaked with blood) indicating cervix beginning to dilate.

** Braxton Hicks contractions are the irregular 'practise' contractions which occur throughout pregnancy, but particularly noticeably in the ninth month.

(the first pattern I've noticed). Pete's going to be half an hour but there's no panic because it could still be hours before we need to go to hospital.

16.40 Contractions coming every three minutes and for the first time feel painful. I get down on all fours and try to sway my hips* to loosen up, and ease the pain. I breathe steadily, and keep calm. I phone hospital and ask for the labour ward. Midwifery Sister tells me to hang on a bit as I haven't been in established labour for long. I tell her differently (after breaking off for another contraction). Can't attend to my daughter any longer; contractions too intense, and I don't want to frighten her. Call neighbour to fetch Susie as arranged. Pete arrives moments later.

17.00 Leave for hospital. Think to myself: 'Goodness if this is early first stage, I can't do it!'** I kneel on the back seat facing rear and gripping the dog guard for all I'm worth. My breathing is not calm, and I am getting noisy!

17.20 Arrive at hospital. Can't get out of car until contraction finishes. No porters so Pete instructed to wheel me in wheelchair to room 15. I plunge to floor beside bed on my knees grabbing gas and air as I go. Try to regain my control and thank God the gas and air helps. I can't bear my clothes any longer and Pete and I rip them off before the next contraction. He tries to get my nightie on but I'm back on the floor with the gas and air. Midwife arrives, summoned by the noise and unaware of our official arrival. She tries to do her paperwork while I keep demanding to know how dilated I am – it is crucial to my staying power! Midwife attempts to do an internal examination with me rocking on my knees, head and hands down into pillows in front of me.

Contractions now every two minutes. Still don't know how far dilated I am. When she asks me if I want to push I realize that yes I do! But pain seems to increase and I start to yell. Midwife manages to calm me and to slow my panic breathing down. She tells me to breathe through nose. Control regained we start to get on with the pushing. Still in kneeling position

* Hip-swaying on all fours is particularly useful for dealing with the pain of the contractions. Jenny had practised this often at her antenatal exercise class.

** Jenny had an epidural anaesthetic when her first baby was born which removed all sensation, so she finds it hard to gauge where she is in labour and how much worse it might get!

but with bean bag in front of me I hold Pete's hand in vice-like grip with each push. I find that as I push down into my bottom my hands push forward into bean bag. It's very hard work but I know I can do it. Midwife unable to find baby's heartbeat so asks me to turn round just to check baby. I resent changing position but do it anyway. Told to feel for baby's head. For some reason I feel afraid of this (perhaps because I would realize the distortion of my body). However, I put my hand down and I'm thrilled – the baby's there! When asked what position I now want to get in for actual delivery, I seem to have lost power of speech, and seem incapable of moving anywhere. So I stay as I am, upright with back and one elbow into bean bag, legs akimbo (naturally). I push again and again the head crowns with me protesting that it hurts! I'm told I can deliver baby onto my tummy but again I need convincing. Pant, pant!, push, push!, and I push my baby out and lift him onto my tummy! Thank goodness I did that! it was wonderful! The time is 18.23, only an hour after we arrived. I instantly feel back in reality; I enjoy the moment to the full. The pain is forgotten and I declare my baby a son. The final motions are then gone through. The midwife delivers the placenta, three skin sutures for a small tear. Pete and I enjoy our baby boy, John, for a few moments, then he goes to make a few phone calls, and I have a cheese sandwich. Then a bath – how civilized!

Reflections
A wonderful birth. Experienced to the full. I think I lost control not knowing how far into labour I was, and it was very difficult to get in the most easing position in the back of the car during what I know now to have been transition. The midwife and sister are in many ways responsible for it being the complete experience it was. They were aware of what I wanted in spite of my being incapable of telling them. Thanks to them I was in a position to deliver my own baby – and that I shall never forget.

Jenny had prepared for natural childbirth and was delighted that she managed it beautifully. As she points out, the attitude of the attendant staff is important and can be a strong factor in how things go. Women worry and fantasize extensively about what their midwife will be like, and midwives worry about women who arrive with inflexible and idealistic aims for their labour. Everyone wants the birth to go safely and happily, but their ideas about what that might mean may vary. Nevertheless, day after day women and midwives up and down the country negotiate these delicate compromises, while also dealing with the labour itself and all the hospital procedures and politics! While it sometimes goes wrong, it often goes right.

While Jenny planned for and prepared a natural birth, Sarah, a doctor herself and with some degree of scepticism, approached the birth of her second child with no particular birthing style in mind.

SARAH

'Natural childbirth!'

Reflections

21.40 I still can't believe how it all happened. It was fantastic. I'm worn out now. ' 'Night, 'night, Elizabeth.' (She looks very different from Mary at that age!)

06.40 What a night! Feeding every one and a half hours, still didn't satisfy Elizabeth, so in the end I gave in and she went to the nursery. I found her there a short while ago – in a room on her own, so guess who'd been making too much noise! I still can't believe how quick it was! She's beginning to look more like Mary.

. . . How quick it was . . .

19 January

08.15 Ring labour ward. ? Ruptured membranes (it really did feel like a 'pop' inside). So, I'm to come in.

09.40 Arrive. Shown to room 8. Not feeling the slightest bit 'labourish'.

10.30 Vaginal examination – hindwater rupture. ARM* forewaters.

* Artificial rupture of membranes. This is sometimes done to speed labour up. It used to be routine during the very 'active management' years of the 1970s and early 1980s. In most hospitals today you are at least consulted as to whether it should happen. Some natural birth lobbies feel it should *never* be done because *any* interference is better avoided.

3 cm and favourable. Still smiling! Walk the floors – few niggles.

11.30 Monitor (CTG)* attached. Niggles don't register. One contraction won't have a baby.

12.00 Simon popped back home for lunch as it may be a long haul and we wouldn't have enough food. I had toast and coffee. I Walk. Walk. Walk. Still smiling!

12.30 Contraction every 10 minutes. Drip looms up?

13.00 Contractions stronger, and now every five minutes. Keep walking!

14.00 Contractions every five minutes for one hour now. Simon encouraging +++, big ones and little ones. Smiles in between.

14.10 Contractions coming closer together – or is that wishful thinking? Coping well with breathing and moving about. On all fours on the floor feels best.

14.15 Still smiling. Simon is fantastic. 'Look at me! – Smile!' Are we really doing it this way? I'd give in if it weren't for Simon's remarks.

14.20 Good grief! contractions getting stronger! About to have internal examination. If I'm only 3–4 cm dilated I'll ask for an epidural (Simon said he wouldn't go for epidural pain relief yet! But I'm the one with the pain!) No Pethidine: I want to stay alert.

14.25 Get on the bed; contractions coming quickly. Can I cope with breathing? Perhaps I should have Pethidine . . . . comment to midwife, 'I need the toilet' (but I just didn't realize the possible significance of it!) Internal exam: 'Try to give a little push', says midwife. 'You're joking!' I think, not wanting a swollen cervix, and convinced I was only 4 cm dilated (but hoping it might be 5 cm or 6 cm). I just didn't believe the midwife. 'How many centimetres?' I ask. 'Do you really want to know?' she asks as she pushes away an anterior lip.** What happened to transition?

As midwives gloved up hurriedly I began to realize they

* CTG is cardiotocograph monitoring which records both the contractions and the fetal heart on a continuous paper graph. A 20-minute 'trace' is often taken on arrival in the labour ward.

** Sometimes a tiny 'lip' of cervix takes ages finally to dilate. In such a situation many midwives will stretch the lip back themselves. Again, while some women are pleased to speed things up, others find it an unwelcome interference. Most natural birth organizations also feel it is an unnecessary interference and to be avoided.

might be telling the truth – that I was fully dilated! And, before I knew it, I was pushing!

But oh the pain!

I didn't realize, the baby's head was just sitting on my perineum – I wouldn't push because I didn't believe the midwives. I put my hand down to press on the parts that hurt rather than to feel for anything, and there the baby was already! Two pushes to a contraction. I could probably have done more, but it hurt so. The midwife was holding my right hand so I was guiding the baby's head myself. Squeezing tightly round Simon with the other arm. A few short pushes and pants. 'Just one more'. I'm still smiling, can't be in labour! 'Just one more'. Head. Anterior shoulder (that hurt!) and I did the rest!

14.45 It's a girl! Elizabeth Louise! And I delivered her! Mary wanted a girl.

No epidural. No drip. No Pethidine.

Natural childbirth!

(And I didn't even want one!)

Jan's baby was also born without her using drugs. The fact that the hospital was busy that night was, she feels, one reason why this happened. It is uncomfortable but probably true that such factors do have a bearing on how things unfold. As well as getting through her labour with great courage, Jan has some useful tips about how to manage large amounts of fluid when the waters break! . . .

JAN

'I have never pushed so hard in my life'

My labour started with a gush at 4 am on 22 December. I awoke thinking my bladder had given out. Half an hour and one bath towel later, I concluded that my membranes had ruptured and that my baby had decided to spend Christmas with us after all (she was not 'due' until 14 January – earliest!) My first contractions began about two hours after the rupture and by 7 am were coming every eight minutes, though varying in strength. It was a doddle, a little breathing and everything was rosy; so much fuss, I thought!

I could not believe the amount of waters one womb could hold. I found it impossible to move around rocking against a wall whilst trying to hold on to my bath towel and dignity. I then had a brainwave and put a terry towelling nappy inside my husband's underpants. This enabled me to dress my bottom half in tracksuit trousers and move around at ease. Mind you I went through four terry nappies, including the one I wore to the hospital – not the height of fashion!

My midwife arrived at 8.30 am. Contractions were still every eight minutes and I was 1 cm dilated. Things were going great: the breathing was getting heavier and I felt a need to move around more. I found being on my knees with my elbows supported, on a chair (at home) and a bean bag (at hospital), the most comfortable positions allowing plenty of movement of my hips and giving me a long torso for the breathing.

By 5 pm my contractions were still every five to six minutes apart but the hospital requested I go in as it had been over 12 hours since my waters broke.* I was about 5 cm dilated; what a blow, I felt sure I must be nearer 7 cm! Jo, my midwife, advised that they would have to put a drip in me to increase the contractions and that it would have to be up to me to refuse, as she could not. As it turned out they were very busy that night and let us get on with it naturally.

Our baby daughter, Laura, had her hand up by her face with her elbow bent which resulted in enormous pressure on my back passage as she moved down the pelvis and her head trapped my cervix which swelled around her forehead. Because of her position she did not move down the pelvis for a long time, but then decided to slip down quickly.

By 10 pm I found I could no longer bear the pain and asked Jo for Pethidine. I had been through the 'jelly' stage and believed I had hit transition but because of the odd time lapse Jo did not think I had. When the hospital midwife arrived she saw that I could no longer resist the urge to push, a feeling that seemed to go from my hair roots to my toe nails! She tested me and said that I was fully dilated with the exception of swollen cervix and I was moved to another delivery room with a high bed so they could monitor me more closely. I found being on my back rather disorientating and very painful but was beyond being able to complain. I had to push on the next contraction while the midwife pulled the rest of the cervix over Laura's head and as Laura's heartbeat was not recovering sufficiently between contractions I was

* Once the waters have gone the sterile protection for the baby has gone too, so there is a danger of infection.

told I had about 10 minutes to get her out. I have never pushed so hard in my life, Roger, my husband, was trying to pop her out like a cork. He held me behind the head and under my left knee and was squeezing me so tight I could hardly get a breath. But within about 10 minutes Laura was delivered onto my stomach and everything was worth it. Laura was born at 10.40 pm on 22 December and weighed in at 6 lb 5 oz. I had to have an episiotomy* due to the short time I had to give birth but it was not as horrific as I had imagined it would be; the worst bit was the stirrups they put your legs in to sew you up at the end.

I can say that not having any drugs during labour, although it can be extremely painful, does make you feel as though you have given birth – not as though you have had your baby extracted from you.

The umbilical cord was not cut until it had stopped beating (about 10 minutes) and Jo ensured that I was not injected to bring the third stage on quickly; the afterbirth came away 10 minutes after the cord was cut.

Jan's comment: 'You feel as though you have given birth, not as though you have had your baby extracted from you' sums up the huge need and desire many women have to be allowed to *give* birth. The dilemma is there – to *give* birth you have to handle a lot of the pain too, and in the thick of that pain it can be hard to remember why you wanted it that way.

As with Jan, this is Kate's first baby. It is quite amazing how efficiently she goes on attending to domestic matters as the strength of the contractions grow within her! . . .

* A cut made in the perineum to enlarge the opening of the vagina. While danger to the baby or the risk of a very bad tear may necessitate an episiotomy, there was a period, again 1970s to 1980s, when they seemed to be performed wholesale. Vociferous protests by women and an increasing body of experimental evidence has lowered the episiotomy rate in most units. Many doctors underestimate how major an intervention this can be. Jan felt reasonably OK, particularly because the reason for the episiotomy was clear. For some women however, it feels nothing short of mutilation. Women often attend antenatal exercise with the express hope of keeping their perineum intact.

KATE

'He was such a miracle'

Looking back, I suppose things started to happen on 8 July, lunchtime, as I was entertaining some colleagues from work in the garden. I said: 'I think he's going to be early'. My EDD by date was, in fact, 8 July but the scan date was 23 July. I'd been going by the latter date all through pregnancy and had only given up work two weeks previously.

I had a show late that night and a low ache started – like a period pain – which waxed and waned irregularly every 20–40 minutes. I still managed to sleep quite well and next morning I reassured my husband that this wasn't really 'it' as it wasn't hurting enough. Tuesday morning I pottered about cleaning the bathroom and sorting some baby clothes. The low aching continued to wax and wane every 15–20 minutes and when Chris phoned me about 10.30 am I again said this wasn't really 'it'. At the same time I was losing what seemed to me rather a lot of pinkish discharge, so I phoned the labour ward about 11.30 am, to be reassured that this was still the show.

After a good lunch of smoked mackerel (how I re-tasted that later!) and potato salad about 1.30 pm, I just stood up to tidy up and 'gush' my waters broke! (Yes, it could be embarrassing in Sainsbury's!) The pains started to get stronger and faster now so I started timing them. Meanwhile, I made some chicken soup and did some ironing. At 3.30 pm they had been coming at six to seven minute intervals for an hour, also the waters seemed to have some blood with it, so I phoned the labour ward and they advised me to come in, but there was no hurry. So, I phoned Chris at work and asked him to come home. Up until this point I'd felt no need to do anything special to cope with the pain except to keep relaxed and keep moving, but now I found I needed to kneel on the floor and lean against a chair and concentrate on breathing. However, I still managed to make Chris some rather misshapened egg sandwiches!

Chris normally only takes 20 minutes to get home but there was a traffic jam and it was an hour (4.30 pm) before he arrived! As he walked in I was kneeling and breathing through a contraction and he panicked and started running up and down the stairs! We managed to get my case together in a few minutes and the journey to hospital took minutes, literally – we arrived at 4.45 pm. The receptionist didn't seem to feel there was any rush, so I spent a couple of contractions leaning against the desk.

My midwife was Laurel from Ebbw Vale, she said: 'We're going to have a really Welsh birth' (Chris and I are both Welsh). After examining me, Laurel pronounced me 9 cm dilated, wonderful! She also reassured me that the blood I was seeing was from the cervix and that the baby was OK. I asked her if I could kneel on all fours on the bed for the 20-minute monitor, but as the contractions came I leaned forward and the fetal heart one came off. Laurel was, however, not at all bothered by the intermittent trace. She also asked me if I wanted the Syntometrine* (for the third stage). I was surprised to be asked and I said I would like to try it without.

The contractions starting coming thick and fast and Laurel brought me a bean bag to lean on. At each contraction I buried my head in the bean bag and concentrated on breathing and on relaxing my pelvis. I found that making low moaning noises helped and Chris helped me by washing my face with cold water and giving me sips of cold water to drink. It seemed like no time at all until I could feel the baby's head in my cervix and I wanted to push. The student midwife who'd been left to keep an eye on us kept telling me to wait until Laurel got back (she was attending some twins next door), when all I wanted to know was if it was OK to push. Soon I couldn't help pushing and Laurel came in and asked if I wanted to deliver as I was on my knees leaning on the bean bag. I was quite happy and so was she after pumping the bed up a bit.

I breathed deeply and pushed while breathing out steadily; it was a wonderful feeling, though Chris said I was making a lot of noise! The crowning was a bit painful due to what turned out to be a small labial tear. Stephen then popped into the world at 6.03 pm – one and a quarter hours after we arrived at the labour ward. He started crying straight away and I turned around and Laurel gave him to me to hold An indescribable feeling! I kept saying to Chris 'I can't believe it!' he was such a miracle (Apgar score 9 and 10).**

* An injection of Syntometrine is routinely given at the moment of delivery in order to cause the womb to contract strongly, expel the placenta, and bleed less profusely. Suckling the baby straight away can have the same effects. Supporters of natural birth feel it is important not to load the system with an unnecessary drug. Medics using Syntometrine often remember that post-partum haemorrhage was a major cause of death in childbearing women not many decades ago. At the moment it is felt that in some circumstances women *should* have Syntometrine. If you are unclear about your own situation, discuss it with your community midwife.

** An assessment of the baby's condition usually taken at one minute and five minutes after birth including observations of heart rate, breathing, colour, muscle tone, and reflex response, expressed as marks out of ten.

The cord was cut straight away as they had to take a cord blood sample as I'm Rhesus negative. The placenta detached quite soon and I delivered it with little effort after about one hour.

After a couple of hours while Laurel, Chris and I inspected and cuddled Stephen, the doctor came in and decided I needed three stitches in the labial tear. She asked me if I wanted the local anaesthetic as I was so brave not needing anything through labour! Having the stitches was the worst part but soon over and they've healed very well.

About 10 pm we arrived on the ward and the midwife said I could have him in bed with me and I lay awake most of the night looking at him and touching him and practising feeding. I just couldn't believe it! A truly wonderful experience.

That wonderful labour flowed in a continuous progression.

For Pat, also expecting her first baby, things were much more frustrating . . .

PAT

'He bathed my face and turned the lights down'

Saturday 8 June. I woke at 7 am feeling incredibly restless, and so got up and made some tea and we read the papers. At about 9 am I had my first contraction. I recognized it as such immediately and was very excited, especially as they continued every five minutes. By the time I was up and about the pains were more regular, but hardly painful at all. 'Great!', I thought, 'this is easy!' Of course this proved to be tempting fate! At about 12.15 with contractions every two minutes we phoned the hospital. They advised us to come in. Once in hospital I was monitored for 20 minutes. The pains were now every three minutes and the monitor showed that they were not very strong. Luckily the midwife, although offering us the option of staying in, suggested that it would probably be better if we went home, as it may be some time before labour was established. With hindsight we were very grateful to her as had I stayed in I'm sure that pressure would have been put on me to speed things up with medical intervention.

Once home I had a bath, watched the television, listened to the record player and we watched contractions come and go! After such a promising start this was a dismal process and I nearly changed my mind about the whole business! During the evening the contractions were a bit longer and a bit more painful and this seemed quite hopeful. I was most comfortable sitting astride a chair with John rubbing my back. At around 8 pm everything stopped. This was really sick-making – I could see myself still having a half-hearted attempt at labour the following month at this rate. At about 10.30 pm we drove at high speed (well nearly) over the ramps into the park and went for a walk in an attempt to get things going again. This was really pleasant. We walked down towards the museum and just moving about got things moving – anyone watching would have thought we were very romantic the number of times we stopped for a cuddle; in actual fact we stopped for the pain sometimes! When we got home the contractions were more painful and about every five minutes – just enough to stop me from sleeping. John went off to bed at midnight, he was bushed with all the excitement, or lack of it! I propped myself forward on a pile of cushions and watched the late night TV rubbish. By 3 am-ish I couldn't get comfortable anywhere and ran a bath. Unfortunately this woke John up. I was finding any position sitting or leaning backwards very uncomfortable. Before I got in the bath my waters broke, or at least leaked a little. And so whilst I sat and moaned about 'What a bloody long time this takes', in the bath, John phoned the hospital who said to come in. By now the contractions were fairly regular and we had the classic 3.30 am trip to hospital. I was convinced that I had hours to go, I was really fed up. I think I must have been in transition. By the time we got to the hospital life was one long pain and I said to John that if they said I was only 1 or 2 cm dilated I was going to have the whole lot – a cocktail of pain relief. I couldn't be bothered to get undressed and John's comforting words were beginning to get up my nose! Yes – I think I was in transition! Can you imagine how fantastic I felt when the midwife examined me and said: 'My goodness you're almost ready to push!'

Looking back the second stage of my labour seems unreal. I moved around the bed a lot, always upright mostly on my knees leaning forward, swaying my hips, making a lot of noise. John held me and bathed my face and turned the lights down which was nice. I told the midwife that they were my pains and not hers when she informed me: 'You've still got a pain, push again!' In fact I'm afraid I was a bit rude to her all the way through. At one point she warned me about making a noise in my throat: 'You'll get a sore throat dear', to which my reply was: 'Sod my bloody throat!' Well your throat doesn't seem that vital when you're in labour does it?! I did apologize to her afterwards but she didn't seem to mind at all – there must be quite a few abusive women about!

I can't remember how long I pushed for but I don't think it was long. I remember John telling me to look down when the baby's head was born. I was kneeling up, John was standing by the bed and he supported me whilst I pulled on him to bear down. One more push and Nicholas David just fell out. I'll never forget the feeling of looking down at him, still attached to me. It was the most satisfying and exciting thing I've ever done in my life. So exciting in fact that I nearly kicked Nicholas off the bed trying to lift my knee and turn around! We waited for a while to have the cord cut, but I put him to the breast straight away and he suckled like an old hand! I had intended to let the placenta come away naturally but in the event I had the injection so that everyone would hurry up and leave John, me and Nicholas alone. I had to have a few stitches – apparently the baby's head didn't tear me, it was his shoulder, and I must admit it wasn't a very good experience being stitched up. Lying there with my feet in stirrups and a big light shining on my bits, I was doubly glad to have given birth in a more natural position.

PS Nicholas was born one hour and 40 minutes after we arrived at the hospital – not bad for a first attempt, eh?!

Jane, with her second child, had a slow start too . . .

JANE

'Breathe in strength, breathe out pain'

04.30 Sleep disturbed by contractions.
06.30 Sleep further disturbed by two-year-old Emily waking.
08.00 Breakfast. Contractions small but irritating, about every five minutes but only for 30 seconds.
09.30 Nick takes Emily swimming.
10.00 Rachel arrives.
Contractions continue as before – no sign of them progressing, getting no longer or closer together, or of them going away!
Finished packing (for the hospital).

Finished the ironing.

11.30 Still the same. I am beginning to feel a bit of a fraud. Everyone was expecting me to have this baby before lunch – now I shall be *cooking* lunch!

12.30 Lunch.

After lunch the contractions very gradually increase in length. And I don't really want anyone else around during them, so I keep getting up and dashing into another room and then coming back for another 5 minutes.

15.00 I go and lie down for a rest. Even small contractions, for nearly 12 hours, get very wearing – and there seems no indication that these might not continue for another 12 hours.

15.30 Emily realizes I'm in bed and wants me to play. Up again!

17.00 Tea-time comes and goes.

17.30 Things seems to be happening – every three minutes now. I phone the hospital. Off we go again.

We arrive and are shown into room 11 and then a midwife and the sister come to examine me. They both have a good prod and then announce: 'You've got a big one there!' – something I'd rather not know at this stage.

The sister announces that she would be back in a minute to do an internal and would break my waters. I asked why. She said that it was something they did routinely. I was a bit dismayed. I hadn't heard that before and said that they hadn't done so last time. I also reminded her that in the past I'd suffered from herpes.* She went to consult with the doctor who said that they wouldn't break the waters or put a monitor on the baby's head. (Actually they did that last time but after the waters had broken. It all seemed a bit odd. Anyway, she wasn't going to break my waters which was just as well as we had decided that we didn't want her to.) I got up onto the bed for her to do an internal. I didn't like them last time and this one was agony. I had been coping with the contractions – now just over one minute – well, standing up and breathing through them, but this was hell.

* If you have active herpes, the baby is usually delivered by Caesarean section to avoid infecting the baby. If you have had herpes in the past it is often a matter of individual consultants' opinion as to how the baby is delivered. If you are in any doubt about this, be sure to talk to a doctor about it during one of your hospital appointments.

Sister suggested gas and air while she did it. So I breathed the Entonox* while she did the examination. When she finished I felt really uncomfortable and a bit heady from the gas and air. I was 4 cm – a bit depressing. She said that the cervix had been well back so she had pulled it forward so that the baby's head would bear down on it and speed things up. I felt I had been violated. I felt that I had been doing OK without any outside help. To me this was an interference I didn't welcome and it really knocked me back. It was as though she was determined to interfere in some way. And she hadn't consulted me first – I suppose that's what made it worse.

19.40 I got back up and started to pace the corridors. Things did seem to speed up. Certainly the contractions became stronger.

20.10 We started to watch TV.

20.30 I was tired and went to try and rest. The contractions were difficult lying down but at least I could rest a little in between.

21.00 Nick came to find me – the TV programme was over! I got up again – back to the TV room and pacing the corridors. The contractions were getting difficult now. I was still upright, though only just! I kept thinking of my antenatal teacher saying: 'spine straight, head up, shoulders down' and of the two most useful phrases: 'Keep your face relaxed'; 'Breathe in strength, breathe out pain'. It all helped. I also remember shaking the pain out of my fingertips.

Now I went back to the room. I was getting a bit noisy and the midwife seemed to think I should stay there. I was quite happy about that. The shift had changed and my new midwife, Amy, was waiting there. She'd had garlic for tea! However she seemed really nice and I felt straight away that we were on the same wavelength.

I was now sitting on the edge of the chair with a bean bag supporting my back. I was still breathing through the contractions OK.

I asked her about lowering the bed and told her that last time I had pushed the baby out kneeling – using Nick to bear down on. I wouldn't be able to do this on a normal delivery bed – I'd be too high to lean on Nick's shoulders. Immediately she said she'd get a low bed – and she did. Thank goodness the shift had changed! I then got onto the bed on all fours, rocking back and

* Proprietary name for mixture of gas (nitrus oxide) and air used as pain relief.

forwards and from knee to knee as things got grim. 'Breathe in strength, breathe out pain.' The bean bag took quite a lot of stick too.

22.00 Another internal. I said that I wasn't keen – but I did want to know how I was doing. So back on my back again, more gas and air and more pain. Amy was great though. She stopped when I asked, and as I commented: 'It's my body'. I was 8–9 cm. She hadn't done all that she wanted – I think she wanted to check the baby's position – but she left it at that. As she said, I was doing better without the gas and air. My waters had broken during the examination.

Back on all fours, beating the bean bag, rocking and breathing. I remember commenting that it was supposed to be easier the second time but, as Amy said, the pain is still the same.

She suggested I tried the gas and air but I was reluctant to change position. I tried it on all fours, only it meant being on all threes instead! I could hold the mask with one hand and still rock. I hated breathing with the mask on. It smells. But I found it helpful to breathe it for the first half of the contraction, drop it and rock through the rest, then panic to find it again ready for the start of the next.

I started to push a bit but not with the same overriding and uncontrollable desire that I recall from last time; just in the middle of the contraction, a bit. Nick called the midwife. Did I want to push or not? I wasn't sure. Was it just wishful thinking? I hoped not. Amy asked if I could try a different position so that the baby's head could bear down on the cervix during the contraction. I ended up sitting on the edge of the bed with Nick on one side and Amy on the other.

How much longer?

Suddenly I just pushed – more of the waters all over the floor. Amy was really anxious to get me back on the bed: 'Second babies slide out quickly,' she said, 'We don't want to drop him on the floor'. So I knelt up on the bed. It was five to midnight. Again I used Nick to bear down against; I think he worked as hard as me. I remember noticing how he braced himself against the bed.

Pushing didn't bring the relief from pain that it did last time. I think the head crowned really quickly. It was then a while before I pushed the head out. It seemed to get stuck half way. I knew I just had to give one really good push. I pushed and pushed. Suddenly it became too much. I let out a scream and then Nick and the sister (called to 'catch') were shouting at me. Apparently I'd nearly sat down on his head! Amy was great. She must have been laying on the floor to be able to see what was going on.

I did push the head out and then I could reach down and hold it. The sister was still helping Nick hold me up so Amy said that she would pass the baby forward to me to catch. (Emily had been born backwards from kneeling.)

12.10 I reached down and did just that. She couldn't see so Nick and I were able to look and discover for ourselves that we had a beautiful son.

I think that the birth went as nearly as possible to what I would have wished. I was glad as I had been feeling that if it didn't this time would I have to try again – the implications of which are obviously enormous.

Jane's comments show just how disruptive and upsetting it can be if procedures are not clear or are carried out without proper agreement. Her rapport with the second midwife (in spite of the garlic!) was obviously much more comfortable.

Jane's final paragraph is also interesting because it shows how having a certain kind of birth can become an overwhelming need in itself. Emily's birth had not been the way Jane wanted it, and she felt that had this labour not been fulfilling, she might have had another baby *just to try to get the birth right*. I do not feel such longings are irrational or peculiar. I came across some extremely powerful video images of deeply instinctual childbirth after two of my children had been born. I felt linked into the power and the glory of birth and sensed the possibility of shifting the context of safe childbirth into something respectful, rather than inherently suspicious, of the natural process of birth. I could feel my hormones triggering like flowering ink-splashes. The urge to go through birth again was irresistible. I did not resist it!

During the same period Jane Fonda broke the fitness taboo on pregnant women, as did, in a rather different spirit, a number of pioneering yoga teachers. Both aerobic-style, and yoga-style exercises were now deemed to be not just permissible, but positively beneficial for pregnant women. Few women however embraced the fitness ethic as passionately as Anna, our next birth storyteller . . .

ANNA

'I tried to get as fit as possible'

Before I conceived I tried to get as fit as possible which was easy as my husband and I both love sport and exercise. I've got my own horse, so I rode him every day, even the night before I went into labour. I galloped him round a hunter trial course and popped over five jumps just to see if I could get things going a bit, but nothing happened.* I continued going to aerobic classes twice a week and I did my last five mile run at 28 weeks, then stopped as my poor bladder couldn't cope with all the pressure.

My dog Carla loved the last few weeks of my pregnancy as I took her on long walks so that I could keep fit.

My contractions first started on Sunday morning at 2 am. They were very mild so I didn't recognize them as the labour pains, as they felt like niggly period cramps. I got out of bed so that I could watch the Olympic games, and I was so excited watching one athlete win her gold medal that I was jumping up and down on the settee and that's when the contractions started to come at regular four to five minute intervals (5 am). I found it useful to walk around the garden during a contraction and then sit down in between.

I started to use the wall to lean against but only for about 10 minutes; then I was more relaxed and comfortable on my hands and knees rocking back and forth.

By 6 am I felt the urge to go for a walk, so I took Carla down the road. I had wanted to walk in to the hospital so I thought I'd time the walk to see how long it would take (my husband David was still asleep and unaware that anything was happening).

As we reached the hospital, the contractions started coming every two minutes and they were getting stronger so we ran back to the house, only stopping to get a newspaper on the way. I'd just got upstairs to the bathroom when my membranes ruptured conveniently over the toilet at 6.30 am.

By this time I felt quite tired so I ran a hot bath and got in and stayed there for half an hour. It really helped me to relax and the contractions

* This really *was* risky. I would *strongly* advise against doing anything like this. The dangers are 1. detaching the placenta leading to severe pain and haemorrhage with associated risk of losing the baby; 2. a clumsy fall resulting in a fractured pelvis.

became more comfortable. David had woken up by then and decided to examine me (he's a GP).

I was so disappointed when he told me my cervix was only 3 cm dilated, I thought it was at least 5 cm. As I was comfortable at home, he said I could stay for a bit longer so I carried on rocking back and forth on my hands and knees, bum in the air, with two towels stuffed between my legs, as I was still leaking water onto the carpet.

By 9 am David hauled me off to hospital, protesting, but he put the seat of the car down so I could carry on rocking.

I was examined by the Sister on arrival and was then 6 cm. They insisted I got onto the bed, but let me carry on rocking back and forth after I'd had the trace [CTG] done. I hated lying on my back as the contractions were uncontrollable and disjointed. It felt like a ton of bricks falling onto my stomach without a rest in between. As soon as the trace was done and I was allowed to carry on rocking, the contractions came at evenly spaced intervals. It was similar to a conveyor belt, the pain started on my left-hand side by my waist, travelled across my abdomen then became stronger and peaked by my belly button then subsided. It gave me at least a minute to flop into a bean bag and recover for the next one.

David was very supportive and only said nice things like 'Brilliant!' 'Not long now!' and he wouldn't let me look at the clock.

The second stage was easier as I was able to sit upright and chat to the midwife. Luckily for me she also had horses so we had a lot in common. She propped me up on the bean bag so I was squatting with lots of pillows behind my back and after two decent pushes Hannah was born at 11.15 am.

I was very lucky not to have an episiotomy. I had pleaded not to have one and got away with a small tear, which after being stitched was unnoticeable and comfortable after three days.

Hannah took to the breast straight away and I was so elated and high after the birth that I had bags of energy and bored everyone silly with stories of my wonderful birth! I stayed in hospital for two days.

I was on a high for 10 days and it helped me cope with my new role. I only put on 11 kg (about 16 lbs) during pregnancy and was back to my normal weight and into my jeans within three days.

Hannah weighed 8 lb 11 oz.

PS I didn't need any analgesia and didn't even think to ask for any.

Not every woman wants to be an athlete during pregnancy, but some, like Anna, do, and thrive on it. Almost all pregnant women, none the less, benefit for regular appropriate exercise – swimming, walking, yoga. It is also sensible, if possible, not to put on enormous amounts of extra weight, although this certainly should be achieved by *healthy eating* rather than *dieting*.

Francesca's is the last of our drug-free hospital deliveries for now. We join her two days before her second baby is due . . .

FRANCESCA

'I promise you the worst pain is over . . .'

20.00 Eating dinner – suddenly feel urge to go to the loo.

20.15 Blood-stained mucus discharge – a show? Ring a friend who says don't panic, could be days yet.

20.30 Wet knickers. Ring hospital – who also say don't panic, finish your meal and come in. Tell husband who says: 'Don't panic' and starts panicking! I feel fine; occasional pains – supper or contractions? We drive to hospital. I try not to get excited – anticipating either a false alarm or the dreaded overnight stay in an antenatal ward.

21.00 Arrive; no rooms available; watch Nine O'clock News in waiting room.

21.20 Midwife appears: horror! She vividly reminds both Derek and I of the midwife who delivered our first-born – a horrendous labour, a horrendous midwife. She asks us to follow her, then vanishes.

21.30 Different midwife arrives (was the chemistry between us and the other one mutual?) This one is charming. Wires me up to fetal monitor and leaves us to it. Can I suck a glucose tablet? Yes! I can also have a cup of tea if I want!! (What a difference – two years ago it was a stern 'No' and water only.)

22.00 She returns. Yes I am in labour – 4 cm dilated (Whoopee!) I agree for her to break my waters. How long will this labour be, I ask? Can hardly believe my ears when she says: 'Only a couple of hours if your contractions keep coming strongly'. She leaves us. At this stage contractions still very bearable and I am my bright, calm, articulate self. This doesn't last long! Stand up, walk around, do the breathing and Derek rubs my lower back during the contractions – wonderful relief. Wee on floor twice; have shower to clean up; midwife quips about potty training. Contractions start to come strong, fast and increasingly painful; recall the awful time last time around; offered gas and air and stoically refuse while privately wondering how on earth I'm going to cope. Between contractions curse ever having decided to have another baby and start to yell. Breathing helps, but increasingly difficult to do as pain becomes worse (NB It's really useful to have your partner clued-up to the breathing, so that he can guide you firmly as the going gets tough.) Derek got confused and started to say 'Breathe in peace, breathe away pain'. Told him in no uncertain terms: 'Breathing in peace' bloody inappropriate, and I needed stamina not peace!

23.00 Feel myself pushing – am I going to loo or having a baby? Midwife reappears. I'm 10 cm dilated and ready to push. Incredible! So soon! Up on bed, she asks if I know how to push. 'No', I say, 'I've no idea.' 'OK', she says, 'if you do exactly as I say, I promise you the worst pain is over and this bit will be relatively easy'. Naively I'm ready to believe her, and amazingly she turns out to be correct. Deep breath at beginning of contraction, then push long and hard once, then again. Keep forgetting what to do; 'Tell me again', I say. Push down for three or four contractions. Someone says: 'We can see baby's head!' Incredible stretching feeling down below; not really painful but tremendously uncomfortable. See tray with scissors; aggressively demand: 'No episiotomy!' Midwife tartly replies she has no intention of doing one unless unavoidable! 'OK' she says, 'Now pant'. Whoosh! a slithery feeling and tremendous relief (like having gone to the loo after being constipated!)

23.30 Baby born!! A girl! 'Is she OK?' 'Yes!' Perineum intact but I need internal stitches as I have torn on the site of previous suture. Feed her, cup of tea, bath and upstairs to the ward elated and exhausted.

2
Birth at Home

Some women strongly and urgently want to give birth at home. For some it is a matter of choosing an environment which is absolutely familiar and comfortable; for others, it is a definite concern to be in a place where interventions and pharmacological pain relief will not be part of the normal pattern and so perhaps be unnecessarily imposed. Still others do not want the birth of a baby wrenched out of the fabric of family life with the enforced separations from partners and other children that hospital birth entails.

There are disagreements about all this. 'What if an emergency arises?' asks the pro-hospital lobby. 'Many emergencies are caused or exacerbated by the hospital system, and there is a flying squad', home birth-committed people reply. I hope those who feel strongly on either side will forgive me for saying that I no longer believe in goodies and baddies regarding this matter. Those who are passionate campaigners for home birth truly believe that both their gut feelings and their empirical data support their case. Those who want every labouring woman in hospital and connected continuously to a fetal heart monitor truly do not want even one baby ever to slip away for want of listening as carefully as possible to the traces of their fragile little lives. Both sides need to examine their consciences vigorously to understand what else is going on on top of the desire to provide the best possible birthing care. Perhaps a longing to control, to dominate, is there, on both sides.

Decisions about home birth are made on the balance of probabilities that mother and baby will be fine. Naturally the interpretation of these criteria vary from area to area, from practitioner to practitioner.

But when it has been negotiated, and the time has come, what of the experience of giving birth at home? Let us hear first from Miranda, whose second baby was born at home . . .

MIRANDA

'I promised to wake them when the real drama started'

I have given birth to this brown-haired, sweet-faced little boy. I'm sitting in bed, with him asleep in the carry-cot beside me, in a totally silent, peaceful house. Everyone else is out and the sense of calm is wonderful.

He was born at 3.40 am. It all went fine, I had him here, at home, as I wanted. Labour started at 9.30 in the evening and it all progressed really quickly and economically – no fiddling in and out of labour for hours on end like I did with Janina. All the squatting practise I did through my pregnancy came in really handy. I wanted nothing more than to squat through all the contractions, leaning against my bed with my head down. The midwife came at 11 pm and the doctor at about 1.30 am and everyone else went to bed . . . after I'd promised to wake them up when the real drama(!) started. I felt much happier just getting on with it on my own: easier to keep the rhythm of the contractions in time with my body if I didn't have to think about anyone else. It was all really manageable until those transition contractions started, then came that sensation of being rocked about uncontrollably on a howling sea of pain and you know that you can do nothing except breathe and wait for it to stop. At that stage I knew I had to lie down, so I called Max and Sandy. Suddenly I remembered I'd left the immersion heater on, so got up to switch it off (funny how silly irrelevant domestic details don't lose their grip even at such a moment) and then collapsed onto my side, into that extraordinary pain-dominated world of the borders of second stage labour. The midwife then discovered that the waters hadn't gone and that she'd left her crochet hook for breaking waters behind, so they used the sharp end of a catheter attachment that the doctor had in his bag instead.

I knew by this stage – just beginning to want to push – that this baby felt very different from Janina; this was feeling a bit too much like hard work and it hurt indescribably. With Janina, I got the pushing urge one minute, pushed twice and out she slithered in a kind of orgasmic ecstasy (me, not her!) With him it felt really difficult to make any progress, even pushing harder, and for longer than I've ever pushed anything in my life before. Eventually his head crowned; by this time I'd nearly bitten Max's hand off. I remember thinking: 'Keep your chin down, don't screw up your face', and screwing up my face as hard as I could in order to bear the effort of pushing again when all I wanted to do was go to sleep. I'd had no pain relief except a couple of puffs of gas and air in the last two transition contractions – not through a sense of altruism – but because I hadn't felt the need. I knew well enough when I *wanted* the gas and air. I think the desire for sleep was simply a need to escape the pain. Anyway, once his head had crowned it became clear that this baby was coming out face upwards – 'face-to-pubes', as the midwife called it. I'd never thought about it but as you no doubt know, it means that the circumference of the bit of head that comes out first is much bigger, also the neck is flexing the wrong way, and the bones in the head don't slide over each other smoothly. No wonder it was hard work getting him out! The midwife was absolutely wonderful. I had a real sense that she was completely in control. If anyone else had told me to pant when she did I'd have kicked them in the face I think. She eased that baby out, leaving me without so much as a graze or a tear, though Sandy who had a bird's eye view, says that everything was stretched to the absolute limit. If I'd been left to do it on my own I know that I'd have ripped apart like an old sheet. I was so desperate to get him out by that stage I'd just have pushed, and carried on pushing until he came out. It was interesting how, having caused me all that pain, I reacted utterly differently to him than I did to Janina when she was born. I fell passionately in love with Janina the minute I saw her. I just felt angry with this baby. I couldn't believe how much he'd hurt me. I was also feeling violently sick – shock-reaction I presume. It took me about half an hour to get over that feeling of anger and begin to take an interest in him; although I had an abstract feeling of pleasure that he was a boy and a glad realization that that was what I'd wanted him to be.

At this stage the doctor announced that this was his first home birth. He wasn't the one I'd been seeing all through antenatal, but I know him well because he did all Janina's postnatal care and injections etc. since then. He had of course done nothing at all except hold on to my left knee when I got the shakes in transition but that's how it should be; an interfering doctor must be hell for a midwife.

So here I am with this little son. My mum and dad and brother were all staying the night he was born and saw him within half an hour of his birth, which delighted them.

What a joyful sense of that baby arriving into a positive house full of loving welcomes – and also of a skilful midwife managing the baby's unusual 'presentation' as he emerged (face up rather than face down from the vagina) so calmly and effectively.

Alison and Sam wanted their second baby to be born at home too, having found a hospital delivery upsetting with their first-born . . .

ALISON AND SAM

'Instead of being shell-shocked and angry we were proud and happy'

Following a short stay on the antenatal ward at 34½ weeks due to leaking hind-waters, I had begun to doubt I would ever experience the home confinement we'd hoped for. A scan had diagnosed poly-hydramnios (excess fluid) and a transverse lie which, together with a haemoglobin level floating around the 10 g mark, seemed to militate against a 'normal' delivery. However, thanks largely to an extremely supportive midwife and GP, I found myself three days past my due date and back on target for a home delivery, although it had meant cancelling two hospital appointments.

I woke Wednesday morning with what I thought to be an upset tummy resulting from over-indulgence at an American supper the night before. Before Sam went to work, we went with Graham (two and a half) to Sainsbury's and stocked the cupboards for the next few weeks. I made Graham a car from all the empty cardboard boxes. I had tummy pains but nothing serious so we carried on as usual, preparing the evening meal and walking to the shops. When Graham went to bed 12–2 pm, I was glad to have the rest too. Throughout the morning I had tried timing the tightenings but I kept forgetting when the last one was and they didn't seem to be at all regular anyway.

I had an antenatal appointment with my community midwife, Francesca, so drove over with Graham about 2.30 pm. I told Francesca I had diarrhoea and she offered to examine me. I was 2 cm dilated, stretchable to 3 cm. Francesca thought something might be happening but I remained unconvinced. The head had been free and high until now but had just started to fix so I comforted myself with the thought that even if it was a tummy bug it was doing something to help.

I'd arranged to spend the afternoon with a midwife friend so I drove over to her house and Graham and Erica spent a happy afternoon in the paddling pool. I was still having irregular contractions but they were only occasionally painful. I was bleeding a little every time I went to the loo but knew this was normal after an internal examination. I drove home at 5.30 pm – it was a half hour drive in the rush hour and I had one or two uncomfortable twinges.

Sam got home from work at 5.45 pm and we all had tea, though I didn't feel very hungry. We went to bed at 11 pm and got up again half an hour later as I couldn't sleep. I suggested we ought to time the contractions in case they were regular; they were – every four minutes.

We decided to come downstairs and watch a video but every time I had a contraction I had accompanying diarrhoea so I had to dash to the loo. Not a very exciting place, I thought, so I got a bucket and Graham's toilet trainer seat and squatted on that so I could watch TV during contractions. Looking back, I think this was very significant in getting a good start in labour as I spent about two hours in this position.

Soon after 1 am, with contractions coming every two or three minutes, we decided to contact Francesca. She arrived 1.30 am, closely followed by the student midwife on call – Minna. On examination at 2 am I was 6 cm dilated. I could hardly believe it! My first labour had moved at a snail's pace and lasted 21 hours.

The contractions were becoming unbearably painful in my back as the baby was in a posterior position.* Francesca suggested I went on all fours over the bean bag and this helped a lot. I was coping well with the contractions by breathing and there was a good happy atmosphere, though we were missing most of the film!

About 3 am we moved upstairs to settle in. I had been so doubtful about being in labour that nothing had been prepared so Sam had to change the bed, put down plastic sheets, and move the furniture around. Shortly after we got settled I had a particularly bad contraction, was very sick and decided to try the gas and air. It was fantastic – I was in control again! We put some music on, resumed chatting. The contractions were getting stronger but I was feeling really pleased with myself. Then, horrors!, the Entonox ran out! The student was sent to the hospital to get some more. Fortunately, we only live a couple of miles from the hospital but initially I panicked at the thought of losing my lifeline. Francesca and Sam were practically shouting at me to breathe with them. I got through the next four contractions by pretending I was a train – a breathing method Francesca had found useful before. On the second of these contractions my membranes ruptured. I was saturated as was the bed and the bean bag. I was concerned the contractions would get worse then but as I was almost fully dilated by then it didn't make much difference.

The student must have driven like a maniac because she was soon back. I was discovered to have an anterior lip on examination so had to huff and puff my way through a few more contractions before I could start pushing. I tried sitting up against the bean bag but the pain in my back was too awful, I insisted on going on all fours. Unfortunately this reduced the urge to push and Francesca wasn't happy with the idea of me pushing on command so we eventually settled on a semi-squat.

* i.e. baby's spine to mother's spine.

Sam sat behind me on a pile of bean bags and cushions and held me under the arms. It took three or four contractions to get it right: I kept pushing backwards and Francesca had to follow us across the bed as I pushed down and she shouted at me to get off her hand! Eventually, we got it right and Rachel slithered out after 20 minutes of pushing. I had a very small tear – a vast improvement on the episiotomy of last time. The worst part was the crowning – I could feel the head there and though I desperately wanted it to be over, the burning sensation made me resist pushing. As she pushed out it was agonizing but I remembered my antenatal teacher saying it would only last 15 to 20 seconds at most. I started counting, hoping it would be less. She was in my arms before I realized it!

Rachel was 8 lb – bigger than everyone had expected. Her Apgars were 9 and 10 so she couldn't have been healthier at birth. Francesca gave me two small stitches once Rachel was cleaned and dressed. It was 6.15 am. Suddenly the door opened and in walked Graham – it was perfect timing. He wasn't at all disturbed by all the blood or the mess I was in. He said 'Hello', to Rachel then told Sam he wanted to go downstairs and have breakfast! I had a bath and returned to a clean bedroom and freshly made-up bed – it was heavenly!

Deciding to have our baby at home was the best thing we could have done. I cannot believe how normal and positive an experience it made labour. Instead of being shell-shocked and angry we were proud and happy. I felt so clever and life carried on fairly much as normal. We are extremely grateful for the wonderful support and enthusiasm of our GP and midwife, who made it all possible.

Gareth and Maggie had planned on a hospital confinement all along. However, they changed their minds at the eleventh hour, for reasons which they explain.

Here is their story . . .

MAGGIE

'She had waited for her own birthday'

When I finally realized, 12 days before my first child was due, that having the birth at home was the only real option, panic set in: 'They will *never* let me do it!'

This was my first child; I was a woman in my mid-thirties and with a history of infertility; it was unthinkable, but we decided that this was what we would go for. Within two days we had it set up. Four days later Rosamund arrived, perfectly and normally, at home.

I had thrived on being pregnant. After unsuccessfully trying for a child during my previous marriage and with several years of infertility tests, I had almost given up hope of ever having a child of my own. Meeting Gareth, my new husband, was a joy and we conceived Rosamund quickly and easily. The pregnancy had gone smoothly and apart from ten days in bed at the beginning when there was a slight chance of a miscarriage, all had gone well.

An important turning point came during the last few months when Gareth and I attended the local hospital – where we were also booked in for the birth – for the antenatal classes. Over the following weeks I noticed a distinct trend. I would go to the classes feeling good and positive, and come away feeling anxious and worried, and depressed.

I think what made me anxious was the attention placed on what could go wrong and all the information about the various types of pain relief. I knew this aspect was important but there was never a word about the incredible event that was going to take place or the joy or amazement of bringing a new person into the world, or the fact that births could take place without major intervention by technology, and had done for thousands of years.

I was definite about having as natural a birth as possible, and although the hospital encouraged this, the reality from friends who had given birth there was that they had all undergone some form of intervention, from TENS* and Pethidine to epidurals and forceps, and the majority of them had also required stitches.

I was worried that I wouldn't be in charge of my child's delivery and that other people would make decisions on my behalf. Although I had briefed Gareth about what I did and did not want, I felt it was going to be hard, if not impossible, to get what I wanted. So it was after the last antenatal class and with an impending sense of doom that Gareth and I sat down and really looked at what was happening.

It took about four hours to come to the conclusion that a home birth was what we really wanted. The next stage was to make it actually happen. The baby was due in 12 days' time and in many ways the shortage of time was to our advantage. In working out our strategy, we

* Trans electrical nerve stimulation. A method of pain control by the application of electrical impulses (via electrodes applied to the skin) to block pain signals to the brain.

assumed that the people in the health authority would be concerned and would try to dissuade us. We also assumed that we could and would have a home birth and that we would be light and definite in our approach to the authorities who, like us, would be concerned that we have a safe delivery; so we had more in common than we had differences.

We thought that once we had made our intentions known, we would need to listen well to their concerns and not expect necessarily, to be listened to ourselves. However, we could do that for one another outside of the various meetings.

It worked well. The supervisor of the midwives whom we met first was very concerned, and couldn't believe that at 38½ weeks we were changing our minds about the place of delivery! However, she reminded us that we did have a choice which was reassuring, and referred us to our local GP as she could not make the final decision.

We knew our GP did not support home births. He was very concerned and did his best to dissuade us. However, we persisted, very lightly, and so he referred us to our consultant at the hospital. By now we were beginning to get a bit disheartened and anxious but we had a marvellous surprise when we met our consultant that afternoon.

He greeted us with the words: 'I understand you want a home birth', and expecting the by-now-familiar follow-on of: 'Well, I don't think this is a good idea, you'll be much safer in the hospital', etc., he instead came out with: 'Well I think that's fine. You have had a good pregnancy and I can't envisage any problems, but even if there are, you are only up the road and we can always get the flying squad out to bring you here. Besides which, it will be good for the midwives'.

What a joy! I was so thrilled that when he asked me to go and give a sample, I came back from the Ladies with the container still in my hand; in my excitement I had forgotten all about it!

So, within two days from that lengthy debate with ourselves, we had our home birth set up. Pat, who was to be our marvellous midwife, came round the following day with an assistant and a bag full of necessary bits, and three days later Rosamund started to arrive. (By now we had the necessary support of a GP from another practice who was local to the hospital.) It was as though she had been waiting for us to sort ourselves out, and once we had, she knew it was safe to come.

In the meantime our families were surprised and a little anxious about our news. I had thought that my mother would be particularly concerned for me, but as usual she came up trumps, knowing that I would do my own thing anyway and that I wouldn't do anything to risk the baby. It was interesting that many of the women we spoke to during those few days who had had children, given their time over said they would have delivered them at home.

Apart from plastic sheets (which I would double in size and quantity another time) and various bits of medical equipment which our midwife brought, we made very little extra preparation for our home birth. We thought a lot about support, both for myself and Gareth during the birth, and asked a good friend of ours, Pauline to be there who had had two of her three children at home and who we knew was confident, reassuring and gentle.

The one day I was wanting to avoid for this birth-day was Gareth's own birthday, but blow me, I woke at about 8 o'clock in the morning on that day with backache and knew that this was it. I couldn't believe it! Gareth opened his presents in between contractions, and the midwife came about midday. Even she couldn't believe the timing! She checked that all was well and said she would come back about 4 o'clock.

In the meantime, it was lovely to wander around my own home, pause for the contractions on my own sofa, eat or drink from my own china whenever I wanted to and listen to my own gentle music. It was very peaceful, quiet and unhurried. A friend called by with a present for Gareth and couldn't believe that she was witnessing a labour!

Pat duly returned. The contractions started to increase from about 6 o'clock onwards and much of the rest of the evening was spent working my way through them. What isn't stated during the antenatal period is that contractions are another word for pain! What is important though is that it is a productive pain, for there is someone amazing at the end of it. I was determined not to have any medical pain relief unless it was absolutely necessary – and being at home precluded a lot of this anyway. I am sure otherwise I would have worked my way through the whole system! Gareth and Pauline were brilliant in keeping my attention on breathing and away from the pain, and giving one another a hand as well.

Pat was a marvellous midwife and just what I wanted. She only intervened when she had to, and between us we timed her listening to the baby's heartbeat at the end of one contraction and before the next, so I could be upright and in my most comfortable position of kneeling. I had thought I would want to be in our bedroom for the birth, but in the event I was happy pottering around the lounge downstairs during the day, and that is where I had her, on the sofa.

The first stage seemed to go on forever, even though everything was normal and on line. The doctor who was our back-up called by at about 9.45 pm and quickly saw that everything was going well and that he wasn't needed, so left, returning just after the birth.

Nearer to midnight the contractions were so intense that I succumbed to gas and air and it was marvellous. I sailed through the next hour or so on cloud nine, waxing lyrical about how marvellous gas and air was, such that a new cylinder had to be brought from the hospital!

When the second stage started, I quickly decided that I wasn't going to hang around for much of this and on about the second or third push, Rosamund started to come out. It all happened so quickly, I couldn't believe that she was out. What a relief! Bless her, she had waited for her own birthday, arriving just after 1 am on the 20th August. I shall never forget being passed this little person and seeing just who had been growing all these months inside me. She was, and is, simply lovely.

The third stage followed quickly and without any interference or assistance. One highlight of the whole event happened after everything had been cleared up. The doctor had visited, Rosamund had been weighed, fed, cuddled, photographed, bathed, cuddled some more and put in her new crib and then Gareth ran me a bath which was easily the best bath I have ever had. It was 3 o'clock in the morning, the water was full to the brim, he had placed two lighted candles either side of the bath and turned the lights off and there I lay, having just delivered my first child in my own home. I felt like Queen Tut!

The following day I woke with Rosamund asleep on my stomach and simply marvelled at what we had achieved.

Those babies arrived at home because their parents planned for them to do so. Some babies just come rather quickly and are born at home anyway! It can be thrilling but also rather terrifying. Marilyn and John's baby did not quite emerge at home, but the labour was so fast that it belongs here, with the 'precipitate' (very fast) births . . .

MARILYN

' "Fully dilated", she says'

Wednesday, 19 August five days overdue.

21.00 One of the first nights I've been to bed, thinking it's *not* going to happen tonight!

Thursday 20 August six days overdue.

07.00 It didn't! Two really minor Braxton Hicks – nothing compared with the strong on/off tightenings of the previous four weeks. A bit cross. Persuade John to let me spend money we don't have on some fabric to make a dress – with buttons for feeding. It'll give me something to do while waiting.

Get up. Off to John Lewis – on foot – to choose pattern and fabric. No air-conditioning – have to sit on floor to amusement of other customers. Walk home – terribly hot, but I still don't feel very imminent.

Coffee at Helen's. Her friend Liz, suggests castor oil. We've tried everything else – and I mean *everything* (naughty, nice and both!) so I take a spoonful at 12 o'clock, followed by lunch –a dubious combination.

15.00 Meri phones: can she bring the kids round and come and keep me company? Yes please! I'll go mad if I wait alone much longer. John wants to spend the afternoon resting in bed. Castor oil hasn't even sent me to the loo, never mind into labour!

15.29 Drinking tea, having filled paddling pool, dragged chairs into garden and smacked poor Nathan (our son) who has poured water on some cushions.

15.30 Very uncomfortable pain, continuous in bum. Is this diarrhoea/labour/head dropping? Go to loo, nothing happens. Go back to tea.

15.40 Decide to get organized, just in case. Pain is turning into contraction-like 'things'. Tell John – he refuses to get excited. Nevertheless, he sits with me, timing contractions while I sit on the loo. One minute long and two minutes apart. This can't be labour, contractions are too close, too quickly.

16.15 A lot of up-and-downing between sitting on the loo and rocking on the floor (an excellent form of pain relief). We phone the hospital. Sister says it all sounds a bit quick; give it an hour, she says, it might go away!

16.25 Phone again; talk through the contraction; I'm coming in – this baby wants out! Organize Meri re. Nathan's routine – thank goodness she's there. John phones parents to summon them from Somerset. Get sandwiches from freezer – we're off!

16.45 Our van is hot like an oven.

First contraction, kneeling on back seat – nearly go

flying! Next one – knee-to-chest position on floor. Feel need to push, so rock forwards and do lots of very loud groaning on the out-breath. This baby is not going to make it to hospital! Trust us to hit the rush hour. Encouraging shouts from John up front help me get through the next few contractions with only once submitting to the pushing urge.

17.00 Abandon John in car park. Race (literally) upstairs; don't know where I am. Reach corridor outside labour ward; back on the floor – groaning away – remarkably controlled considering I'm in a major panic. Rather overwhelmed passers-by go and warn labour ward. John arrives. I run in. Another trip to the floor, more groaning and two startled midwives rush out, calling me 'Poppet' and encouraging me to 'hang on a minute'!

17.10 No spare rooms; am guided into community room; undressed and put onto enormously high bed. Then – thank heavens for gas and air. Groan into that, to take away pushing urge, while examined. 'Fully dilated', midwife says, as she forcibly holds baby in. Waters are broken.

17.15 Big push: there's his head! I hold it, wonderful; panic turns to relief. Very painful while I wait for next contraction, head half out. Here we go! Big pushes, out head pops; he's breathing, good. Lots of dark hair. Come on contraction, another push, slither, another boy and he's crying. He's put on my tummy. We've only been there 10 minutes and I stroke him in disbelief. I've heard of speedy deliveries but this is ridiculous. Next time (??) we'll forget the castor oil! I clean Matthew up and John cuts the cord.

20.30 – 21.30 I'm finally stitched! One hell of a wait [three hours]. Two days later, I'm going home – feeling terrific. Matthew is wonderful and I'm looking forward to many happy years in my family of four.

A birth as fast as this is sometimes followed by a 'shock' reaction such as shaking or shivering. It can also leave the mother, and perhaps the baby too, feeling rather disorientated, but plenty of cuddles and quiet time together help to restore equilibrium on both sides.

Lucy had her first baby in an English hospital, and was booked to have her second in a Belgian one. Her athletic tendencies are similar to Anna's!

LUCY

'The baby seemed amazed'

Day before – 21 August. Lovely hot day.

09.00 One-hour aerobic class outside.

14.00 26 lengths outdoor swimming pool.

Evening: more swimming in my friend Di's pool.

Birthday – 22 August

One contraction in the night, painful, could this be it? A few more.

02.45 Looked at the time. Felt excited. Contractions felt painful. Tried different things to relieve the pain. Found I couldn't breathe through them – unlike previous labour; decided I'd forgotten what to do. Got into a routine of getting out of bed with each contraction and going into the bathroom where I could lean on the sink and make circular motions with my hips or rock backwards and forwards. Felt quite calm. Did not wake up Mark who had not slept well the night before and I knew we would have a long day ahead of us. Diarrhoea twice. Tried to sleep in between contractions as I had done last time but found that just as I was drifting off another contraction would come. I would then have to make my weary journey to the bathroom until the contraction had gone and I could lie back in bed again (bliss). Sometimes I could hardly stay in bed at all – one contraction following another, then another. Other times I thought I had 20 minutes between contractions – I thought, but I was not timing them. Wondered if it was a false labour because the contractions were irregular.

07.15 Mark woke up. He asked me if I was all right. I replied that I was in labour. 'Are you sure?', he asked. I said I thought so but that the contractions did not seem regular. He was excited but panicky at the same time. He timed my contractions as one every five minutes but short and irregular. Now that Mark was awake I started making more fuss about my contractions. Staggering and moaning around the end of the bed as I went to the bathroom with each contraction. I tried to do the yoga '*Mmmm*' mantra with each out-breath – but really I was not doing very well at all with my breathing.

I wanted to wash my hair. Mark agreed a bath would be a good idea as it would relax me and give him time to get ready to go to hospital. The bath water felt lovely and warm, especially on my stomach. But with each contraction I'd have to get up quickly, grab hold of the sink, lean forward and rock my hips in any direction. Got Mark to massage my buttocks which became very tense with each contraction.

After my bath I timed three contractions in five minutes between 8.30 and 8.35 – I was amazed at their frequency. Mark insisted we went to hospital. Then with the next contraction my waters broke. Last time when my waters broke it marked the end of the first stage. Mark told me to get dressed quickly. This I had great trouble doing. I then wanted to comb my hair but I was told firmly that there was not time.

I asked Mark to phone Priscilla (a physiotherapist from the hospital who had given me antenatal classes and would help with the labour with massage and by suggesting positions, movements and sounds to use to get through the contractions). He also asked her to tell the hospital we were coming in. As Mark was on the phone to her I said I wanted to push! What should we do? Mark wanted to call an ambulance but was worried there was not enough time. I suggested that he got Rina, our neighbour who is a nurse. He ran next door and asked her to call an ambulance and a doctor. Meanwhile I was on my own and thought the best thing to do would be to get on my knees with my head down and to pant so as not to push. But then with the next contraction I felt my whole body lurch upward with a huge push and I could feel the head crown. I screamed not with pain or fear but because Mark might miss the birth. Then I yelled: 'Mark!' I struggled to take off my knickers. Katherine, Mark's 16-year-old sister who was staying with us ran next door and got Mark. By the time Mark and Katherine had come back I was on my feet. I then had another contraction and the head came out further! I put my hands down to feel it. The head came out completely with the next contraction, I could see it between my legs. I was standing up with my knees slightly bent. I held onto Katherine who was in front of me. Mark got behind me to hold the baby as it came out. Katherine reminded Mark to check the cord wasn't round the baby's neck – it wasn't. Then, with the next contraction the baby slithered out into Mark's hands. The baby was pink with eyes and mouth closed. I thought it was dead. She didn't cry at first, like her brother Andrew had done. We were all anxious for her to breathe. Mark tilted her head slightly down to drain out any mucus. He wondered if he should hold her upside down and smack her!! Then to our relief she cried a little and started breathing. I then noticed to my surprise and joy she was a girl. I felt absolute relief (blissful peace) that the contractions had stopped as if there had been a continual loud noise for hours which had suddenly been turned off.

I tried to feed the baby but she was not interested. Rina arrived from next door.

08.45 Two ambulance men turned up. Dr Beling arrived; she clamped the cord. I had asked if I could deliver the placenta before the cord was clamped but was told 'No'. Dr Beling asked me if I wanted to deliver the placenta. I felt no contractions but put my arms round Rina and one of the ambulance men who were conveniently next to me for a supported squat and delivered the placenta quite easily into my mixing bowl.

I asked Dr Beling if I needed stitches – she said she thought so. I had a wash and got ready to go to hospital. Then I went downstairs where I found a very excited Andrew running around with his toy ambulance – pointing to the flashing lights of the real ambulance outside. I asked him for a kiss and showed him his new sister.

It was a lovely hot sunny day. I walked to the ambulance where there was quite a reception party of neighbours and villagers in the street. I sat down in the ambulance and tried to feed my new baby. Then the ambulance left, lights flashing and siren going. So much for dimmed lights and peace and quiet. The baby seemed amazed and looked round at all that was going on.

Arrived at hospital where the baby finally fed. The baby was weighed and checked. Mark, Katherine and Andrew arrived. Mark bathed the baby. The doctor said I needed stitches. When I'd been thoroughly washed, he said: 'I'm sorry'. I thought, 'Oh no he's found a big internal tear'. But he said: 'I'm mistaken, you don't need any stitches'. I was really pleased and proud of myself. Last time I had said 'Never again!' This time I felt much more positive about the whole experience.

If your baby or your partner's baby is arriving very rapidly, call an ambulance on 999.

A rapid birth will probably require very little intervention. However, if the baby has a loop or loops of umbilical cord around its neck, slip them over its head *before* the shoulders are born.

Dry the baby and wrap it warmly, especially covering the head. Do not attempt to expel the afterbirth. If it comes of its own accord place it in a bag and put it near the baby but DO NOT cut the cord.

To help the baby breathe if it does not do so immediately, gently tip the baby's head down so that any secretions drain out. Gently breathe onto the baby's chest or flick his or her feet. If the baby still does not breathe, do mouth to mouth-and-nose artificial resuscitation VERY GENTLY using only the air in your cheeks. Blowing hard into a baby's lungs will harm them.

MIRANDA (Again, with third baby)

'I thought: . . . "There's nothing left to hold him in now" '

I suppose it really started when I woke up in the middle of Friday night feeling peculiar sensations inside me. The baby was very active and I had that hot, pre-menstrual pain. 'Hmm', I thought, and went back to sleep. Saturday morning I had diarrhoea, and thought it was maybe just a stomach upset, while mentally noting that one does clear out one's system before childbirth. So I went to Tesco's with the children and did the week's shopping, noticing that the stomach ache got worse – rather rhythmically – every five or 10 minutes. Got home and disappeared up to the loft to hunt desperately for first-size baby clothes, sheets, blankets, carry-cot etc. etc. Sent Max to Mothercare to buy new ones because the ones I emerged with were stale, dank and dusty. Put three loads of washing through the machine; convinced by now that the baby was on its way. At about 2.30 I had the show and decided maybe the time had come to call the midwife. She came about 3.30, examined me and took the wind absolutely out of my sails, saying I hadn't even started dilating, that his head wasn't engaged (which I knew – the bump was way up high still), and that, although she was sure the baby was on his way, he was unlikely to be born before Monday or Sunday at the earliest! The *very* earliest she was prepared to predict was the early hours of Sunday morning.

Now, it should be noted here that I trusted this midwife's judgement completely. She is very experienced and she delivered Luke (second baby) with a degree of skill and confidence that I'll never forget. And I'm sure she was correct when saying that I wasn't dilating at the time she examined me.

Anyway, I thought, OK, I'm not sitting around here all afternoon with this going on inside me. If I'm going to have a slow, painful labour we might as well go out. So we walked into town, just me, Max and Janina which was very nice, and most unusual to have her on her own. We did some shopping and had a cup of tea. By the time we left the café the contractions were coming every two/three minutes and were painful enough that I had to consciously breathe to deal with them. Walking home was not a comfortable experience, although there was something oddly reassuring about being out in the world where everything was going on as usual. The strange thing is that, such was my confidence in the accuracy of the midwife's judgement that I still believed the contractions would probably slow down or stop for a while soon. This, despite all the evidence to the contrary: my body was quite clearly going into action with all the smooth speed and inevitability of an express train pulling out of a station. Looking back on it I'm amazed that I didn't phone the midwife again as soon as I got home. Anyway, I didn't. I ironed a couple of nighties, hung up some washing, stopping every couple of minutes to hang on to something, remembering vaguely about what's supposed to help.

Then I got in the bath – where the pain rapidly became indescribable. Luckily, by this time Janina's friend Amy and Amy's dad and Luke had got back. Amy's dad soon realized that he'd better keep all three children out of the way. Max was trying to persuade me to let go of him so he could call the midwife. I somehow don't remember how I got out of the bath. Max called the midwife at 7 pm – me still trying to believe I wasn't really in labour, despite having 'stormy waves out at sea' style contractions. After all, I thought, my waters haven't even gone yet. Five minutes after Max phoned the midwife the waters went – pop! – floods of fluid all over the bedroom carpet. And I thought: 'There's nothing left to hold him in now' . . . I was right by then to be scared of the pain. Without any kind of pain relief, even gas and air, it was dire. So I screamed and screamed and screamed – aware vaguely of the children downstairs and the neighbours out in the garden. And I suppose it's true that screaming releases some kind of natural pain relief. It certainly made it *just* possible to bear – given that I had no choice.

Then I started to want to push. Still no widwife. Up till then I'd been kneeling – knees spread wide leaning on the bed, but my feet were going numb, so I crawled onto the bed and said to Max: 'It's no good, I've got to push!' And did. I could feel the baby's head sliding down as

I pushed, then slipping up a bit when I stopped. Then came the moment when I knew if I pushed again his head would be born. This bit all happened very fast – five minutes for the second stage I reckon.

I shouted to Max: 'Go and grab his head!' At that moment the midwife walked/ran (!) through the door, just in time to deliver his head. It was a relief to see her. I'd been worrying somewhere about whether Max would know about cords round babies' necks, and trying to remember about panting. Max apparently, meanwhile, was wishing he'd read the books! I'm sure Max would have delivered Thomas perfectly competently if he'd had to. Thomas didn't have the cord round his neck, and started breathing as soon as his head emerged, so there were no complications at all. The midwife, of course, was terribly apologetic. Nothing was ready so she had to literally tip everything out of the bags. Thomas got wrapped in the towel that Max had used to try and soak up some of the fluid from under me on the floor when the waters went! I'm pleased not to have torn at all. Thomas obviously didn't come out too fast otherwise I would have. He was officially two-and-a-half weeks early, but was clearly full term. He weighed 7 lbs 12 oz at birth and was 21 inches long, and there was no vernix on him. He was, and is, wonderful.

3
Early Arrivals and Induced Labours

This chapter concerns births of babies who are born prematurely – i.e. where for one reason or another the labour process starts before 38 weeks plus of pregnancy, and a baby is born who is extra vulnerable because of having less fat to keep warm with, less mature lungs to breathe with, and less strength overall – and at the other end of the spectrum, births where the labour process does not start on its own at all and is kick-started into action by induction. Both sets of circumstances impose different concerns, different challenges, and create different experiences.

Let us begin with William and Caroline . . .

WILLIAM AND CAROLINE

'I was amazed how small he was'

My labour started quite unexpectedly at 35½ weeks. My membranes ruptured whilst asleep in bed at 1 am. There was no doubt about it: I felt a warm gush, turned over to put on the light, heard a popping noise and saw another rush of clear fluid. I phoned the hospital to give them my details and say we'd be going in.

William and I had a cup of coffee and tried to calm ourselves. We were both shocked and a bit dazed – as well as being tired! We dashed around the house adding things like the camera and Walkman to my half-packed suitcase.

We arrived at the hospital about half an hour later. We were shown into a 'first stage' room. I gave a specimen of urine, changed into my nightdress and waited to be admitted. I had a trace of the baby's heart rate done. It was fine. The monitor also showed that I was having very mild contractions approximately one every 10 minutes. Had I not had the monitor to watch I don't think I'd have known I was having them. The doctor arrived and did a speculum examination to confirm that my membranes had ruptured. I remember feeling a bit scared but also dazed, as if it wasn't really happening to me! David was sent home to sleep and I to the antenatal ward to be reviewed in the morning. I felt disappointed that I was stuck in hospital and my labour hadn't even started. I hadn't bargained on being induced. By the time I was settled on the ward and William had gone it was about 3 am. I was in an all empty six-bedded ward on my own.

I tried to lie down and sleep but had too much on my mind. I began to feel contractions though not strong. I practised breathing through them. At 4 am I wandered along the corridor to the nursery with ten pence in my hand intending to ask if I could phone my husband. I wanted his company but felt guilty about depriving him of sleep if we had a long labour ahead of us. Sister persuaded me to have a warm bath which I did. I had a couple of contractions whilst in the bath though not particularly painful. I went back to bed, but felt restless, and so paced the ward.

At about 5 am my contractions were more regular and stronger. I breathed in strength, breathed away fear and pain as discussed in the classes and it really did help me psychologically. I phoned my husband at 5.45 am. I told him it was beginning to hurt and that I was starving, please could be bring in some food! He had been asleep and said he would be half an hour.

After I'd put down the receiver and used my only ten pence, I started to contract more strongly. I walked around the ward. I did slow, steady breathing. I rubbed my abdomen in a soothing circular motion. I tried various positions – leaning against the wall, over the bed table etc. – but none of these helped. The only thing I found I could do was to sway free-standing.

During the time I spent on the antenatal ward I went to the toilet, had my bowels open and passed urine several times. I remember telling myself I must try and go hourly. I noticed blood on my pad.

I felt the pain of my contractions in my lower back and in a line across the top of my pubic hair, where my cervix was dilating. I tried not to panic but I desperately wanted William to arrive. I talked to the baby and begged it not to hurt me!

The midwife that had admitted me earlier popped in to see how I was doing, saw that I was having strong contractions and said she'd be back soon. William arrived at about 6.30 am and I burst into tears.

I told him off for taking so long. He said he'd had to get dressed, have a shave and make the sandwiches! He offered me one but I was no longer hungry but in excruciating pain during these contractions. They were coming every few minutes.

I asked William to rub my back and leaned against him. Poor chap – everything he seemed to do was wrong and I got very ratty with him!

He said I should have told him that I was having contractions not just that it hurt and he'd have come sooner!

I pressed the bell for someone to take us back to the labour ward. I was losing control. I continued to breathe but was unable to stop myself shouting out now. I walked around to the first stage room but don't remember how I did it. Once inside the room I was asked to get onto the bed to be examined.

However, I was having another painful contraction and with that one I squatted on the floor and gave a push. The midwife did a quick vaginal examination and confirmed that my cervix was fully dilated and that I could start pushing in earnest. I'm sure I would have done anyway by that stage. My body had taken over.

I was wheeled straight round to a small back theatre as both delivery rooms were in use. I didn't notice my surroundings anyway. My midwife was excellent – very calm and supportive. I pushed on all fours with my head buried in the pillows. It felt as if I were trying to push a boulder uphill through my rectum. It hurt a lot and I was very tempted to give up. William wiped my face in between contractions.

The head came down beautifully and I actually only gave about eight strong pushes before Anthony was born. I remember saying: 'Please don't cut me', to the midwife and kept asking how much of the head she and William could see. I couldn't believe it at first when she said the size of a 50p piece – it felt like a football!

The crowning of the head felt like a searing burning pain. The head was delivered very slowly and obviously with great skill as my perineum was intact (I did have a small vaginal tear that needed a few stitches though). Anthony was passed through my legs so that I could see him.

I was amazed how small he was. I had expected to have a big baby and the fact that I was only 35½ weeks hadn't really registered. Needless to say it was a huge relief when it was all over.

I was extremely lucky to have had such a short labour. Though the speed of it and the power of the contractions were rather alarming I hardly had time to complain. Had I been asked to turn over and sit up I couldn't have. I hadn't planned to have an all-fours delivery. I thought it was unladylike and that I'd be too inhibited, but I thoroughly recommend anyone to try it!

~

Caroline is indeed a very dignified and poised woman and it is interesting to hear how her reservations about being on all fours disappeared as the huge sensations of labour took over.

Her labour began with a gush – the waters clearly breaking. Amanda had a much more worrying time because instead of a burst of waters she had a steady trickle . . .

AMANDA

'Eleven people were saying "Push, push!" '

We moved into our new house on 2 August thinking we had plenty of time to get straight before the baby was born (he was due on 7 October). However, two and a half weeks after we had moved in and only seven and a half months pregnant I began 'leaking'. I remembered what my antenatal teacher had told us in class and I contacted the hospital. This was Thursday morning. They said come straight in, but after examining me they said it wasn't the waters so I could go home, suggesting it was my bladder! I felt stupid and waddled off to town to do some shopping and began to get wetter and wetter, by the time I got back to the car all my clothes were wet, so I assumed it was my bladder and rushed home to change. This leaking continued all Thursday night, all day Friday, all day Saturday and all day Sunday. All the time I was very worried as I remember the antenatal teacher telling us about the distinct smell of amniotic fluid. I knew in my own mind that this leaking was not my bladder but that it was the waters. I began noticing that the baby wasn't moving quite as much, I was dreadfully worried.* The hospital said only to go back if there was any sign of blood.

By Sunday the leaking was so bad that I was using five pads each day and quite able to 'wring them out', then thankfully a few spots of blood, my long-awaited excuse to go back to the hospital. It was 6 o'clock on Sunday evening, 25th August, and I was just 34 weeks pregnant. The staff seemed a little curt with me at first, I felt I was wasting their time, however when a doctor examined me he said I was 4 cm dilated and asked me when the waters broke!! Twenty minutes later and I was 6 cm dilated. The midwife I had was not at all sympathetic to 'natural childbirth'. I was kneeling up on the bed when she arrived, she told me to sit back! She didn't look the type to argue with, I sat back. Thirty minutes later and I was 9 cm dilated and only the midwife and my husband were in the room. I closed my eyes for a second and the next time I opened them I counted 11 people!! I

* If leaking plus decreasing fetal movement happens to you, go back to hospital and insist on being re-examined, whatever *anybody* says.

closed my eyes again quickly. They had also wheeled in lots of equipment.

By now I was very anxious to say the least, perhaps the baby wouldn't survive. Four days leaking and very little movement from the baby I felt sure things had gone wrong. All at once all 11 people were saying: 'Push, push!' They all looked so silly I had to close my eyes. But thinking about being stitched up if I didn't push I began to push very hard, then there he was screaming his head off, a beautiful little boy, a very 'little' boy. They grabbed him so quickly I hardly had time to see him. By now everyone was ignoring me and my demands of: 'Is he all right?, is he all right?' Only the midwife stayed by my side.

As quickly as they had come into the room the uninvited guests left. For them the excitement was over, the baby was 'normal'. I think they had expected a very tiny baby perhaps only weighing two or three pounds. As it was Philip's weight was 5 lb 5 oz but he had to go to Special Care for 24 hours as he was quite cold. It seemed ages before they let me see him and by the time I did he was fully wrapped in clothes. I would have liked to have held him naked the minute he was born, however I was just glad he was OK.

The midwife passed him to me to see if he would feed. For some reason I didn't expect him to, so when he began sucking I yelled: 'He's doing it, he's doing it!' and Simon and I began laughing. Then, much to the embarrassment of the midwife, we began singing *Happy Birthday* to baby Philip. I felt very happy. Although the birth hadn't been as 'active' as I'd have liked I did manage to get by without having stitches or any drugs or gas and air, and labour only lasted two hours from start to finish. I considered myself lucky.

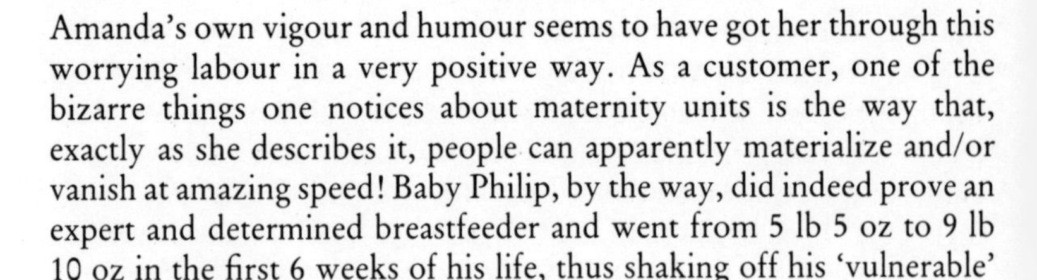

Amanda's own vigour and humour seems to have got her through this worrying labour in a very positive way. As a customer, one of the bizarre things one notices about maternity units is the way that, exactly as she describes it, people can apparently materialize and/or vanish at amazing speed! Baby Philip, by the way, did indeed prove an expert and determined breastfeeder and went from 5 lb 5 oz to 9 lb 10 oz in the first 6 weeks of his life, thus shaking off his 'vulnerable' image rather fast.

The next baby, nicknamed 'Fish' while still in the womb by his mother Serena, really was tiny. At 32 weeks Serena has already had two episodes of vaginal bleeding . . .

SERENA

'3 lbs 14 oz of beauty'

I was transferred to hospital X from hospital Y last Wednesday and once again confined to bed rest. Feeling healthy and well and with the leaking stopped, I did find it hard to be confined within the hospital and found myself becoming more and more anxious. But, in many ways, it was an invaluable time for I became more aware of my relation to 'Fish' and the uniqueness of being a mother. I was discharged on Monday evening with the proviso that I return immediately should I begin bleeding again.

After spending a beautiful evening at home – it was good simply to relax and be with Daniel – I woke up the following morning to find I was leaking a mixture of liquor* and blood. The amount was worrying, so I decided to re-admit myself and was once again fixed onto a monitor in the delivery ward. I began contracting at about 6 pm and was found to be 2 cm dilated but there was no pain and by 10 pm they decided to send me up to the antenatal ward. By 4 o'clock the following morning, after no sleep, the contractions were becoming decidedly stronger and I was sent back down to delivery, and after being wired to the monitor, and given an internal (4 cm dilated) they suggested I try to sleep.

However, I found it much more comfortable to rock myself on the bed and it was good to be alone and be aware of the dawn and relative peace. Daniel arrived at about 7 am by which time the contractions were coming much more regularly and with the window left wide open (to deter the staff!) he began to massage my back between contractions. I couldn't move around the room because of the amount of blood I was losing and they had earlier fixed a monitor onto the baby's head. However, almost every doctor, midwife, nurse, student I had come into contact with, I had spoken about having a natural birth and though they had a whole contingency of plans as it was a premature birth (32 weeks) the midwife was very willing to let me find the most comfortable position on the bed and was both practical and encouraging. With a bean bag behind and half the bed folded away they placed a chair at the end of the bed. I was able to sit up with my feet resting on the chair arms. From then on everything seemed to progress rapidly. Feelings of nausea were replaced by huge waves of pain flooding my body and I was learning to understand that this pain was necessary

* Another name for amniotic fluid.

(inevitable) but could be used constructively. I tried to concentrate on it and by 9 am I could feel the sensation of the head pressing down upon the perineum. The bed was re-extended, I was given an injection for the episiotomy – which I didn't want but the midwife explained that it was necessary for a premature baby – however she didn't have time to cut as the head crowned. I reached down to touch it, the contractions became completely still, and then with one final surge, the child emerged: he had pushed himself into the world at 9.13 am on a beautiful morning.

They had to cut the cord immediately but that moment of seeing him laying on his back, crying or laughing, hands and arms waving and kicking was pure joy. Then he was immediately placed in a rescusitaire and taken to Special Care.

I had to have several stitches for two small tears and then they took me to the Special Care Unit to see him: 3 lb 14 oz of beauty. He will probably be in the Unit until his expected birthday. However, he is already out of the ventilator and yesterday we were able to hold him and wash and change his tiny nappy! It was such a good feeling and Daniel is completely in love with our little boy.

There is going to be a lot to adapt to over the following few weeks – with love and happiness and a slight ache!

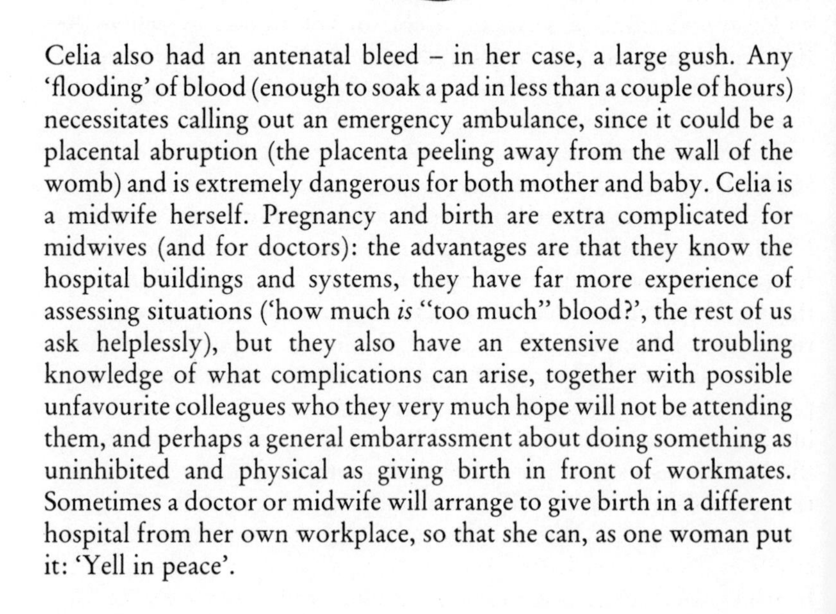

Celia also had an antenatal bleed – in her case, a large gush. Any 'flooding' of blood (enough to soak a pad in less than a couple of hours) necessitates calling out an emergency ambulance, since it could be a placental abruption (the placenta peeling away from the wall of the womb) and is extremely dangerous for both mother and baby. Celia is a midwife herself. Pregnancy and birth are extra complicated for midwives (and for doctors): the advantages are that they know the hospital buildings and systems, they have far more experience of assessing situations ('how much *is* "too much" blood?', the rest of us ask helplessly), but they also have an extensive and troubling knowledge of what complications can arise, together with possible unfavourite colleagues who they very much hope will not be attending them, and perhaps a general embarrassment about doing something as uninhibited and physical as giving birth in front of workmates. Sometimes a doctor or midwife will arrange to give birth in a different hospital from her own workplace, so that she can, as one woman put it: 'Yell in peace'.

Here is Celia's story . . .

CELIA

'A skinned rabbit, but a very loveable one'

Having had a trouble-free pregnancy and enjoying going to antenatal yoga sessions, it came as rather a shock when at 1 am on 11 November (Edward being due on December 10) I found I was bleeding heavily having just gone to bed. It was completely painless but it was literally gushing out and when I tried moving it came more rapidly. Luckily my husband had just got in from work and was, poor thing, panicking enough for both of us. I was amazed how calmly I told him to call for an ambulance and to phone the hospital to tell them we were on our way, although inside I was terrified for Edward's safety.

The relief of hearing Edward's little heartbeat on the monitor in labour ward was phenomenal. My blood loss had slowed by then, so I was sent to the antenatal ward for the night, having been examined internally and found that my membranes were still intact.

I was on bed rest all morning, sitting attached to a monitor to see how Edward was getting on. I was so happy to listen to his heart clip-clopping away. I had an ultrasound scan to see whether they could find where the bleeding was coming from. It was difficult to judge as Edward was lying in front of the placenta. They found, however, that he was a bit underweight and undersized for the 36 weeks' gestation I was.

Back on the antenatal ward I was given another internal examination and the doctor found I was 2 cm dilated and 'favourable', i.e., my cervix was ripening for labour. I had only been aware of Braxton Hicks-type contractions but they were clearly doing something. Edward's heart rate had been dipping slightly with each tightening so the doctors decided it would be best to hurry things along a bit by rupturing my membranes.

I went down to labour ward and my waters were broken at 3.00 pm. By this time I was 3 cm dilated. The tightenings now became more like how I had imagined contractions to feel. I began to have to breathe through them – using the deep breathing (in through the nose and out through the mouth) learned at antenatal yoga classes.

I should have said that I had a drip up as I was not allowed to eat anything in case I needed a Caesarian section. Together with no sleep from the night before, I did not have an awful lot of reserve energy for my contractions, but the glucose in the drip made me feel a whole lot better.

I was rather concerned that I would need Syntocinon* to speed my labour up, as although my contractions were beginning to be more regular they only lasted about 20 seconds and each one made Edward's heart rate dip down. I had a fetal scalp electrode attached to his head to make the monitoring of his heart rate more accurate. Arranging my drip and the electrode plus lead, I found that by kneeling upright I could make my contractions stronger and more frequent. When I was actually experiencing a contraction I would go on 'all fours' and breathe through it – breathing in strength and breathing away pain. My husband helped enormously by rubbing the small of my back while I rocked my hips from side to side. I found this position made the contractions a lot easier to cope with. If I had been told to sit down I would have wanted an epidural.

By 6 pm I was still 3 cm dilated but my cervix had thinned and was being taken up as part of the uterus. The doctor was satisfied with the progress I'd made and so did not start the Syntocinon.

By 9 pm I was 6–7 cm dilated. I was so pleased as by now the contractions were biting and had they not been dilating my cervix I think I would have needed some form of pain relief. This progress encouraged me to continue with the breathing method.

Up until this time I had had a lovely Irish midwife looking after me, and then the midwife I had asked to look after me was available to come and take over. Laurel was great. She sensed I wanted no interruptions during my contractions so said nothing in order that I could concentrate on my breathing.

The urge to push came at about 11.30 pm. I remember thinking it would probably come soon as I had been feeling very shaky – 'transition', I thought. With his head stetching me, I breathed hard to cope with the feeling, and his head came out!

Edward was born at one minute past midnight. Laurel helped my husband deliver his shoulder and the rest of him onto my tummy. I could not believe how small he was – 4 lb 2 oz – rather like a skinned rabbit, but a very loveable one. When the placenta was delivered, Laurel found quite a large retroplacental clot – the source of the bleed I had had.

Edward came up to the ward with me but unfortunately had to go to Special Care because he did not have enough energy to maintain his own blood sugar levels. He became very poorly over the next 24 hours

* Propretary name for oxytocin, the hormone causing the uterus to contact.

but is now making a good recovery. I suppose it made us realize how very precious he is, right from the very start.

I can't wait to get him home – it will be the best Christmas present ever!

Pamela's second labour threatened to start as worryingly early as her first . . .

PAMELA

'The main thing is for him to get much stronger'

My first baby, Richard, was born 10 weeks early, so I improved by three weeks – Henry was born seven weeks early! I had had contractions all the way through this pregnancy, and was admitted when only 24 weeks, and so was quite relieved to carry the baby as long as I did. However, that did not compensate for having 'lost' yet another baby to the Special Care Baby Unit, and it is disappointing to have another sick baby – but Henry is really holding his own – after two days on a ventilator he is now out of his incubator, still being tube fed, but beginning to take my expressed breast milk in a bottle, so we are very grateful that we have such an excellent SCBU for him to be in.

But back to the birth – that was the compensation: it was wonderful compared to Richard's birth. At 30 weeks his was a very 'hi-tech' affair and the whole thing was taken out of my control – which is of course fair enough with a very delicate baby. But *this* time, despite a consultant telling me, whilst I was contracting, that I'd have to have: '. . . another automatic forceps and episiotomy', because of him being premature, I had a wonderful, supportive midwife who understood my panic reaction to this and said she was prepared to see if we could get away without it, and would try to hold out as long as possible – and we did: I had no drugs, no stitches and just a small tear which is now fine. So, at 10 days after the birth I feel physically completely recovered – if not mentally!

I started having contractions regularly. I had the classic signs: low backache, period pain-type aches, going to the loo over and over again, so although I had had contractions throughout the pregnancy I knew this was different and guessed the baby would be born soon, no matter what people did to stop it. I spent the afternoon organizing –

putting the last stock of cooking in the freezer, alerting our babysitter for possibly being called up in the middle of the night. As soon as my husband got in from work I horrified him by saying I was just about to phone the hospital to ask to be admitted!

But to my horror, despite my 'history', the labour Ward told me to stay at home and phone my GP – a really odd decision considering I was only just 33 weeks pregnant. Fortunately, my GP was available and immediately sorted things out and phoned back telling me to get going quickly! I was monitored in the labour ward and was told I was contracting every 10 minutes (I knew this already!!) but wasn't given an internal examination as they didn't want to 'get me going' unnecessarily and was sent up to the antenatal ward, where I continued to have stronger contractions.

An obstetrician was called and gave me an injection of Omnopon* – designed to knock out the contractions and slow things down. Unfortunately it did nothing to stop the contractions, but knocked me out – I quite literally 'fainted away' and woke up having contractions every five minutes, and being *very* sick at about 2 am in the morning. I was given an internal examination then and was informed, to my amazement, that I was 5 cm dilated. They were going to phone up my husband and get him back fast (he'd gone home to put Richard to bed, having settled me into the antenatal ward, convinced it was yet another false alarm!)

I was taken back to the labour ward and put on a monitor again. The baby was holding up really well with a good regular heart rate, but I had to stay strapped up to the monitor then – from 2 am until I delivered at 11 am. This was hard as I had to stay in virtually the same position or else the trace was lost. But every 10 minutes or so I shifted from my back to my side, which did relieve the backache a bit.

But now for the bit which most people will not believe! Maybe it was because I'd had contractions all the way through my pregnancy and so my body just took it in its stride. But when I was told that I was fully dilated I can honestly say that I had not encountered pain. OK, the contractions were uncomfortable and took my breath away, but I really felt in control the whole time and never considered any pain relief. The yoga breathing really, really helped and surprisingly, thinking about the contractions and getting into the feeling, helped too.

The second stage was a different story! As the baby was so small I had no desire to push and an hour went by and nothing happened. The

* A morphine-like drug.

baby's heart rate kept dipping and my wonderful midwife, who had resisted all orders from the doctors said: 'Shall we just get on with this?' and I finally agreed to her breaking my waters – which was not at all unpleasant after all – and following threats from her that they would have to get the baby out quickly now, with forceps, if I didn't start pushing, I did push the baby out in about 15 minutes. We were allowed to hold Henry for about half an hour before he was taken to Special Care, and this helped, although it was incredibly sad to have to part with him. But the main thing is now for him to grow up a bit and get much stronger. I do want people to know that even if you do get complications in your pregnancy and delivery that if you can say how you hope things can go, people will listen and the birth can still be a very good experience.

Parents of these early, tiny babies emphasize how fierce a tenderness they feel for their sons and daughters. Birth, even of a robust baby, pulls us back from the casual brutality of everyday life to an acute awareness of how precious life is. When the baby is more fragile, the hold on life more tenuous, that feeling is even more intense. The innocence of a new baby is immensely powerful too: the grubby compromises, mistakes, and malevolences of adulthood show up in all their nastiness. For many of us, a fresh start seems possible with birth: although the ups and downs of looking after a young baby soon knock the romance out of it, we can still treasure the *real* chance to be spiritually and psychologically reborn along with the births of our children.

The great wash of emotion following childbirth can affect people's behaviour in a risky way as well as an empowering one. In the hospital where I worked we put some time into getting partners of birthing women to reorientate themselves and get firmly in touch with reality before, for example, driving off in their cars. We also encouraged partners to think carefully about any important financial or professional decisions taken around the time of birth. One senior police officer said: 'After my first child was born, I made some odd decisions. I let all sorts of people go because I just didn't believe they were going to do anything bad again!' Luckily, this particular effect of the afterglow did not last long!

While some labours start easily and will not settle down and wait for the appropriate time, others will not get going at all. In these cases labour may be induced by inserting a hormone pessary into the vagina, or by dripping hormone directly into a vein via a very narrow tube. If a pessary is sufficient, the rhythm of contractions is often 'natural', i.e. building up in intensity on a steady curve. If a drip is used some women find their contractions become very strong very quickly, which can be frightening.

Induction may be performed if the waters have broken (because the sterile seal around the baby is gone) or if the baby is very overdue (because an ageing placenta may be working less well) or if for any other reason it is felt that the baby would be safer born than remaining in the womb.

In Honor's case it was because her waters had gone. Honor is a doctor herself but she still was not all that clear whether her membranes were leaking or not. Even medically trained women find that labour is not always signed like a motorway (last exit to first stage)! Also, like Celia, there is a strange double-awareness for pregnant health professionals where something which they can observe as a professional feels very different and is sometimes more puzzling as a human experience . . .

HONOR

'Her heart rate was rock steady'

My waters went (in retrospect) on the Friday afternoon but only a trickle so I failed to realize what was happening. I even attended the antenatal clinic later that afternoon, mentioned that I felt a little damp, and was told that increased secretions were normal towards term! At that visit my blood pressure was still high, so a community midwife was fixed to check it the following Monday. So I trotted off home again, still leaking and by 11 pm decided this was definitely not normal, but I still wasn't sure, so I phoned labour ward and in we went. It all seemed quite unreal, as we had imagined (and planned for) that I would be going in actually *in* labour, and possibly in a hurry. As it was, we spent a leisurely half hour making coffee and sandwiches and crushing up ice cubes! And not a single contraction.

In the labour ward, the sister on duty confirmed that the waters had gone, but that I was only 1 cm dilated and not contracting. A 20-minute heart trace on the baby was fine so I was merely sent round to the ward and put to bed for the night. (At this stage, her head was still not engaged at all, but from various clinic examinations, it seemed likely that she was back to front, i.e., occipitoposterior).

That night was pretty foul, really. We decided Steve should go home to get some sleep but we were both so excited, knowing that things were imminent. The pillows were hard, there was quite a lot of noise, and I barely slept. By morning I had a lousy headache and in fact Steve spent the first part of the labour massaging my aching neck! I was re-examined at 10 am and was found to be 3 cm dilated and although I was having the occasional tightening I still wasn't really in labour. Because of the danger of infection getting in through the ruptured amniotic sac, they decided not to wait so I went back to labour ward to be induced. I had been dreading this as I had imagined it would be more painful than a natural labour and also because I thought the drip and monitors would stop me being 'active', but I was wrong on both counts!

The first two to three hours were scarcely painful at all and I was happy resting and conserving my energy. Steve reappeared bearing yet more crushed ice and all the tapes we had prepared of soothing music – Debussy, Vaughan Williams and Mozart and Brahms – which helped a lot. By 2 pm I was 4 cm dilated and although the baby had to have a scalp monitor put in (the external monitor wasn't providing a good trace), her head was still so free, they still couldn't tell which way round it was.

I moved to a chair at that point. Gradually, the contractions increased in intensity. I found the best thing was standing leaning over the delivery table and swaying or rocking. The pelvic floor preparation was really useful here as I was able to check that I was relaxing it each time. Between contractions I flopped on the chair. Steve was a fantastic help. Between changing tapes and fetching yet more ice, his presence was a great support as well as providing the physical help needed to move the chair each time I stood up/sat down and to get me up and down.

After a couple of hours my legs felt too tired for this so they put the mattress on the floor and I knelt leaning over the chair, flopping down between times. I must say the midwife who was with us was lovely – not interfering when we seemed to be managing on our own, and being very positive about trying different positions. I went through a sick/giddy phase ('Aha! transition', I thought) but then a new pain appeared – fairly excruciating backache, quite different from the contractions, which were copeable with. It felt like the baby was trying to come out through my lower back, and breathing/rocking etc. didn't help too much.

At 5 pm I was re-examined Good news: I was 8 cm; bad news she was occipitoposterior and her head was still high. It was put to me that to get to full dilation was going to take a lot longer because of her position and that if she didn't turn, forceps would be needed. That would need an epidural, so would I like one now as I seemed to be using a lot of energy coping with the pain? All of which was true, though I had been very unkeen on the idea of an epidural. I must say that it was presented very much as a choice and it was for me to decide. Steve and I had a quick chat and I agreed to have one.

In fact it was absolutely the right thing at the time – it was painless going in, it was really effective and it allowed me three hours' rest. I should also say that, despite my advance reservations, I found the fetal heart monitor very reassuring. The baby's heart rate was rock steady throughout, so nobody was in a hurry to intervene.

By 9–9.30 pm the epidural was wearing off a bit, and I was re-examined. I was fully dilated and hooray! her head had turned round. So I started pushing. Obviously the urge to bear down was not really there to start with but I could feel the 'top' of each contraction and could tell when I was pushing in the right direction (of course I was on the couch, because of the epidural, but well propped up). As her head came down, I began to be able to feel it, which also helped. We had a mirror, so I was able to see her head appear (I helped the descent by being violently sick!) Once her head was born (which was painless) I could touch it – and then all at once she appeared, all lovely and was planted on my tummy! She gave one cry then opened her eyes and looked around, very pink and alert. She seemed curious rather than upset. We were speechless with joy and Steve was in tears. Then a bonus: no episiotomy and no tears or stitches! (The midwife who had been with me all day stayed one and a half hours late to deliver Catherine. Steve told me afterwards how careful she had been to get her out without my tearing.)

Because of the long period with ruptured membranes, baby Catherine had to have various swabs taken to look for infection (and there wasn't any) but apart from that we were able to hold her for ages – she wasn't bothered or anything. Then round to the ward to give Catherine her first feed (she suckled hungrily straight away) and for me to have several cups of tea.

Melissa's labour was also induced when her waters broke but no regular contractions followed . . .

MELISSA

'This was my hour'

My labour with Rose started on 24 November at 1.15 am. I was suddenly awoken from sleep with the sensation that the whole of my lower back was on fire. This was followed by a show. I then settled into a routine of contractions, one every five minutes for three hours. During this time, when the contractions were largely fairly mild, I found swaying my hips very soothing. In between the contractions I would rest, head on arms on the side of the bed kneeling back on my heels. A hot bath during this time was also extremely pleasant and very soothing.

Unfortunately, after a good start, I then fell asleep and the contractions disappeared! During the course of the following day I was aware of a small leakage and being unsure if my waters had broken we eventually went to the hospital on the evening of 24 November. I was contracting irregularly, every half-hour or so at this time.

I was finally examined by a registrar at about 9 pm who confirmed that my membranes *had* ruptured, probably many hours earlier, and that due to the risk that prolonged rupture may pose for the baby, he felt my labour ought to be augmented with an oxytocin drip. I, of course, agreed but began to feel at that time that I might be losing control of my labour. It was not going to be as I had imagined.

At 1 am, the drip was finally established and labour began. The midwife allowed Robin and I to do exactly what we wanted, and I again chose a position of sitting back on my heels leaning forward on a bean bag. During the contractions I was able to rise onto all fours, or kneeling upright with my arms round Robin's neck I used breathing and hip swaying, which were very nice; Robin's slow, deep massage of my lower back was lovely and perhaps the most helpful.

After two hours, the intensity of the contractions was such that I felt they were beginning to overpower me – perhaps because I was on a drip – they had built up to great intensity very rapidly. It was suggested that I should have an epidural, to which I agreed. I had very mixed feelings about this: I felt I was losing control of my labour; I was surrounded by machines, each with its own particular bleeping noise and I felt I was lost among them. I was unable to move because my legs were dead (from the epidural) and I ended up crouched in the worst possible position. I no longer had any control over my contractions or my pain. I felt very frightened. I wanted to cry but was unable to. On the other hand, I knew that I could not cope with the contractions as they were and could not see that there was any sense in being a martyr to the pain. The labour might be long and I had to conserve my strength for later.

The epidural was only a partial success. From 8 cm it gave little pain relief; it kept my legs useless and back inaccessible to massage. I then relied on breathing alone, and with Robin's help managed to breathe away my fear and gain some courage and strength for the second stage.

The second stage was different. I was lying on my back (as I know you shouldn't!) but I was in control again. I was able to push despite the epidural and, within the limitations of my condition, was able to be active in this stage. This was my hour. The delivery was beautiful. I had my hand on her head as she was born and was allowed to deliver her body myself. The birth was magical: she came up onto my stomach, and the moment was worth *every* pain. The midwives were superb and the birth was peaceful and beautiful, with all the machines turned off and just the four, and then five, of us in the room.

We can feel with relief the room quietening and darkening and the focus of the birth returning to mother and baby as the technology recedes. As Melissa says, the birth itself really was 'her hour'.

Sometimes the induction process does not go so smoothly, and the birth is further medicated. This is what happened to Janet . . .

JANET

'I feel like something out of an old Ealing comedy'

I was feeling determined not to be alarmed by any pains as I had had two false alarms. The first had been two weeks before; a show of bright red blood and quite a lot of it. I was called in to the labour ward and put on the monitor which found I was having quite sizeable 'tightenings' and would probably go into labour. However, the blood was found to be probably due to cervical irritation caused by antithrush pessaries, the tightenings stopped, everyone expressed a different opinion, and I went home. I had, a week later, two sessions of painful contractions every 20 minutes. Both stopped after an hour and we breathed again. I resolved to put pregnancy and childbirth to the back of my mind lest I was becoming obsessional!

Then, on 8 February:

03.45 I had been aware of backache and vague pre-period type discomfort earlier on. As I lay in bed I felt something pop! – my waters breaking?

We phoned the labour ward. I was totally calm and laid back and stressed I was not having regular painful contractions. They said to get in within two hours.

06.00 Arrive at labour ward. Monitor showed baby OK; contractions mild. Midwife explained the situation; internal examination confirmed waters had gone.

09.00 Posse of doctors arrive and I feel like something out of an old Ealing comedy as they discuss me. It is decided that, because of increasing risk of infection, I should be induced with a hormone drip. I accept this as inevitable. I do some relaxation before being hooked up.

09.30 Drip inserted and hormone gradually increased each hour till it stands at 32 – the maximum, I am told. Boredom and frustration set in as the contractions are still not my idea of very painful. I am repeatedly offered pain relief, but do not want or need it.

15.00 Contractions regular and fairly painful. Patrick is getting anxious but can't go anywhere for long.

17.00 The male doctor arrives. He says things are not going well, the contractions are not strong enough. Before he can double the drip to 64 he must insert a catheter into the uterus which gives a more sensitive reading of its response to avoid 'overdosing'. I do not find this reassuring. I ask if it is painful. He says: 'No more than a vaginal examination, but you can have some gas and air'.

In my case this was being economical with the truth. Because my cervix was 'posterior' and very hard to get at, and because I was now only 1 cm dilated, the experience was appalling. It was very painful and extremely distressing. The doctor muttered his remarks not to me but the midwife and finally gave up. He apologized and I collapsed sobbing and shaking. Patrick mobilized all his rock-like qualities to help me over this one.

I stress this procedure is not normally so bad – it just was unfortunate in my case.

The contractions are now more regular and more painful but I still don't want Pethidine. I actually *want* to feel some bad pain! Sister says she has a good feeling that I will now 'crack on in labour' and that things will progress. The breathing and gently rocking and swaying help a lot. I use the chair next to the drip and the bean bag.

19.30 Doctors return. They decide they should increase the hormone, so must do another internal examination with a view to inserting the dreaded catheter. I am horrified and so, I suspect, is the doctor. I'm told it's sure to be easier as I will have dilated.

21.15 Bloody awful once again; he only does an internal and finds I am not much advanced from before. The fact that I haven't had any drugs except gas and air for two internal examinations indicates to him that I am not really in labour! He says before he can decide what to do he must consult his superior who has more experience and longer fingers. This sounds ominous. While I wait for Long Fingers I force myself to concentrate on breathing and relaxing. I do some rocking and stretching as best I can despite my bionic appearance. Patrick is wonderful, as he has been all through, urging me to breathe in strength and breathe out pain and fear. That takes a hell of a lot of breathing out.

21.30 Doctor arrives and is extremely nice – speaks directly to me and is calm and gentle. He does the vaginal examination and says I am 2 cm dilated. He puts the alternatives to me: catheter and double hormone or a Caesarian section. He asks how long we have tried for a baby; I say 10 years. He looks at me long and hard. 'Are you thinking I should go for the section?', I ask, 'Yes', comes the reply, 'but it's totally up to you'. Patrick and I discuss it for a bit and decide I cannot go through hours more of this with no guarantee of success. We decide on a section. In view of what has happened I insist on a general anaesthetic. Patrick finally looks shell-shocked and goes for a walk.

22.20 I am shaved a bit, prepared and told exactly what will happen. I feel a whole lot better. I am still a bit shaken up, but after some whacks of antacid and antiemetic [antisickness], I prepare for Thomas' introduction to life. Patrick comes with me to the door of theatre and will be handed Thomas as soon as he is out while they do me up. He smiles and kisses me.

23.10 Through a stoned haze I am aware of smiles and happiness. Patrick is sitting in a green gown next to me in the recovery room holding our 8 lb 6 oz bundle of pink healthy baby. He looks ecstatic. My mouth won't work with my brain but I ask the normal questions and touch him in disbelief. As soon as I am off the trolley and on the bed they put Thomas to the breast, and he sucks at once.

This, of course, was worth everything. I can't really believe that this animated, demanding and loveable creature is ours and here at last. Parts of the labour experience were not good, but it is an experience of such absolute joy to have one's own child pass from the womb to your arms that it wipes out all the negative elements. Although I would have preferred a vaginal birth, I don't feel I failed because I had a Caesarian. I did my best and finally chose an option that was much less stressful for Thomas. Sitting looking at him now I just feel very happy and extremely lucky.

It is very hard to know what good guidelines for parents are regarding Caesarian section. The growing numbers of sections practised as 'defensive' medicine (i.e. primarily to avoid litigation) are of course worrying; but in Janet's case it so obviously seems like her own 'gut feeling' choice, with which she was entirely happy, as well as the medically preferred option. Janet says: 'I don't feel I failed', and this feels important. The *down* side of the work which natural birth lobbyists (amongst whom I would identify myself) have done in increasing choice, decreasing unnecessary interventions, and facilitation and empowering dignity for parents, babies, and medical practitioners alike, is that 'achieving' a 'natural' birth can become a sort of hurdle women feel they have to jump in order to 'succeed'. My first yoga teacher broke through all my preconceptions about exercise by saying: 'In yoga there's no competition and no prize'.

Something similar needs to happen around childbirth too. There is no Identikit perfect birth. There is only a 'best possible' birth where safety and sensitivity are available in the optimum measures for each particular labour.

Siobhan felt particularly vulnerable as her due date approached. This is why . . .

SIOBHAN

'The relief was indescribable'

I feel that a little background information is necessary for this birth report to enable the reader to appreciate the reason for certain decisions we made. In August last year, I had an emergency Caesarian at 37 weeks as the baby had stopped moving and, unfortunately, this resulted in stillbirth. The baby, a girl, was a good size, 6 lb 9 oz, but even after a post-mortem, no reason could be given for the tragedy. It can be appreciated that when we made the decision to try again, we were very nervous to say the least. In fact, I could have done with a little longer to get used to the idea but as I was already 33, we felt that it would be prudent to go ahead as we could not guarantee I would get pregnant again straight away. As it happened, I did and unfortunately I was only four weeks later in my dates than last time which made everything more difficult at each milestone.

At 16 weeks, I had the usual blood test which showed a low level of alphafetoprotein and we were informed that this could indicate Down's syndrome. I was offered an amniocentesis and after waiting four weeks (which seemed like four years) for the results, it was thankfully normal. Then a few weeks later, a bright spot showed up on the scan and they were not sure what this could be. Visions of brain tumours immediately came to my mind and I was sent to the big hospital for a better scan. They assured me there that they were 'fairly confident' that it was a harmless cyst and that it would disappear at about 28 weeks. To our relief it did so.

I did feel that prior to this the level of care was a bit laid back, but they explained that there was little they could do prior to 28 weeks. I appreciated this but a little more reassurance would have gone a long way to alleviating my apprehension in view of my history. I think the system is to blame really as when I jumped up and down a bit, they seemed genuinely surprised and immediately I was given the best possible attention and everybody seemed really concerned. I think you just have to stand up for yourself but this is not always easy.

At 36 weeks I elected to attend the hospital for monitoring every other day in order to ensure that the baby's heart beat was OK. Although nerve-wracking it helped reassure me and I got to know most of the nursing staff which was very nice when I was eventually admitted for the birth, as they were like old friends. The consultant was very helpful in explaining all my options and agreed to allow me to go overdue in the hope that I would start off naturally as I was not keen to be induced. After six days overdue though my nerve finally cracked and I agreed to induction.

We arrived at the hospital at 8.30 am on 11 October and the midwife introduced herself and the usual observations were taken. I was shown into a room where, assuming there were no problems, the birth would take place. Everything was explained carefully to me and I felt in no way pressurized to accept anything I was not happy with. I explained that I wanted to try and have a natural birth, if possible, but I had to accept that I would have to be monitored continuously once labour got going in view of the problems last time. I felt this was a shame as it meant my movements would be restricted but it seemed the safest thing. A pessary was inserted and I was told to walk about and keep active as this should start the contractions. By lunchtime nothing had happened, but since I had had a show about a week earlier the cervix was quite stretchy and 2 cm dilated, so they decided to break the waters. This was quite painless but still did not start the contractions, so they asked if I minded having a drip set up. This was duly done and also a saline* drip was put up in case another Caesarian was needed. This set things going almost immediately as it transpired that I was sensitive to the drug in the drip and contractions came thick and fast without giving me time to get used to them. Fortunately, my husband was there to help me cope and we took it in turns to inhale the gas and air.** I didn't feel this was having much effect and the contractions were becoming too much for me to cope with. They adjusted the drip to half strength but this had no effect and by late afternoon I was climbing the walls and telling my husband to shut up.

By this time the midwives had changed shifts. I got a tremendous urge to push. They did a quick examination and found that the baby's head was facing upwards which was causing the urge. There was no way in the position I was in (sitting up) that I could stop pushing even with the breathing and obviously, with all the monitors I could not get my head down to relieve the pressure. There was also a monitor on the baby's head. They were quite worried that I could not stop pushing as I was only 5 cm dilated and I was panicking in case I did some damage, so they suggested an epidural. I agreed to this and it was done straightaway although I found it difficult to keep still while it was set up. It was a painless procedure and the effects were miraculous.

* Salt water solution. Most of the fluid in the body is made up of just such a solution so the drip allows mother to recieve 1. fluids bypassing her stomach (with risk of vomiting) 2. any drugs in case of emergency.

** *Not* normal labour ward practice!

Everything seemed to stop and the relief was indescribable. I was sat up with a cup of tea beaming at everybody in no time while watching the contractions come and go on the monitor. It was about 11.15 pm by this time. Over the next couple of hours I dilated to 10 cm and they told me to start pushing. Even though they turned the epidural down, I found this hard to do as I could feel nothing although my efforts did bring the baby down a little way; all I succeeded in doing was giving myself enormous piles!

After 40 minutes of pushing they decided to consult the consultant and he advised forceps. I was quite willing by this time as it was obviously the only way anything was going to happen and with the epidural, I felt nothing other than a dragging sensation, and my son emerged, all 9 lb 8 oz of him. No wonder he was a problem to push! The episiotomy was sewn up straight away and I was washed and taken down to the main ward to sleep off the effects of the epidural. This took about four hours to get the feeling back in my legs and there were no other ill-effects. The stitches and piles were very painful for about a week but I found witch hazel a great help.

To sum up, I couldn't have had a more hi-tech birth if I had tried, but I was grateful for all that was done and pleased that I had avoided another Caesarian.

So we leave Siobhan with her lovely big baby boy; hi-tech birth, but human miracle intact.

4
Births Where Drugs Are Used, and Assisted Deliveries

Many women prepare themselves for birth without drugs, but then for one reason or another change their minds during labour. Sometimes, as in Louise's case, it is a very laid back decision with very laid back results. She used Pethidine and gas and air (Entonox) . . .

LOUISE

'She turned her head and looked up at him'

After having a week or so of period-type pains I went to bed on Thursday evening and whilst thinking about the last minute bits and pieces I still needed to buy, I felt a pop in the lower abdominal area and knew something had happened. I got up and went to the loo and noticed clear white jelly stuff and knew this was my show. This was just before midnight. The period pains seemed to get a bit stronger and I thought I was leaking fluid but was not really sure. I was on my own at the time as my husband was on 'nights'. I wanted to tell him what had happened as I felt quite excited. Whilst trying to decide whether or not he should come home the pains were getting stronger and seemed to be coming about every five minutes. I decided that if it was not too difficult for him I would quite like him to come home. He phoned ten minutes later to say he was on his way by which time I had no doubt whatsoever that I wanted him home. After about half an hour the contractions were coming every five minutes and were 'taking the smile off my face'. I can remember thinking: 'Where are my breaks for packing etc.?!' I tried leaning and rocking and started deep breathing. My husband wanted to phone the hospital but I said 'No!' The whole thing had only started about an hour and a half ago. The contractions were now every two to three minutes, my husband asked me again if he should phone the hospital. When I didn't answer him he took this as a 'Yes!' We arrived at hospital at 2.15 am and I had the last delivery room!

I was examined and was told I was 3 cm dilated. I was put on a monitor, and luckily still just about had the state of mind to ask if I could sit on the end of the bed. This enabled me to rock through the contractions which I found really helpful. The monitoring was unsuccessful to start with as the machine would not function properly. They brought in another machine so the whole process started again. After the monitor was taken away I tried a few different positions but nothing really seemed to help. Contractions had stayed steady at about every two or three minutes so I decided to go back to rocking on the end of the bed and deep breathing. I found the breathing really helpful but would say that it was done without consciously thinking about it – my body seemed to take control of itself. I was offered Pethidine but refused at this point. I was offered it again some time later, the midwife said I had a long way to go and shouldn't wear myself out too soon. By this time I thought 'What the hell!'

After the Pethidine I sat back on the bed against a bean bag. The Pethidine had a calming, relaxing effect which definitely helped me relax in between each contraction. A couple of hours later the midwife suggested I tried the gas and air. I was reluctant at first as I didn't like the smell of the rubber seal. A little while later I thought it worth another try after which I felt pleasantly relaxed.

During labour I had a midwife who checked on me at various intervals throughout the night; she finished at 7.30 am. Just before finishing she gave me another small dose of Pethidine.

After 7.30 I was attended by a midwifery sister and student midwife who stayed with me all the time. I got to a stage where it was almost impossible not to push during a contraction. Luckily the student midwife had the sense to fetch the sister who examined me; she mentioned a lip so I knew what the situation was. She then said she would try to open my cervix that last little bit. This she managed to do without causing me any discomfort. She did not tell me to push at this stage but to breathe deeply through each contraction. I heard her explain to the student that by doing this she saved me twenty minutes of pushing time (apparently by doing this my body did the pushing for me). I will be eternally grateful to her for this as towards the end my contractions practically stopped so I needed all this saved energy for the end. After about 15–20 minutes I was told to push; but by this time the contractions had practically stopped – just when I needed them! After another couple of pushes I was told the baby's head had crowned, the sister called my husband to look. The next push and her head appeared. The cord was round her neck so I had a bit of huffing to do so they could slip it over her head. My husband said she turned her head and looked at him (something he will never forget for the rest of his life). She slithered out of my body at 9.30 am; what a wonderful feeling! She was a bit drowsy; the sister said I shouldn't have been given the last dose of Pethidine. She was given some oxygen and was OK. A few minutes later the placenta came away – that was a lovely feeling as well. I had three or four stitches due to grazing and was very pleased and grateful to the sister that I didn't have an episiotomy. When she was born I looked at the clock – it was 9.30 am, just as the antenatal yoga class was starting. I felt I wanted to run up and tell everyone but didn't think the sister would have been very impressed! All in all I was very pleased with the birth. Maybe I shouldn't have had the extra Pethidine but at the time I felt I really needed it.

My feelings now, a few days after the birth.

The feelings towards our daughter are almost overwhelming. This wasn't 'instant' for me but took a day or so. For someone who likes 12 hours sleep per day, I can't believe how I actually want to get up in the night to see to her. I am breastfeeding and although we are still learning, I find it one of the most enjoyable and satisfying things I have ever experienced.

Charlotte was very committed to a drug-free birth, but found the pain of labour far stronger than her expectations – a fact she shares very frankly. A warm bath helped for a while, and then she used Entonox . . .

CHARLOTTE

'It's only one day, and it's a pain you don't remember'

On 27 March I had twinges down below. I presumed it was the head engaging. By the evening I had a dull ache in my lower abdomen and slight backache which got worse as the evening went on. I ignored it and went to bed. I had to rock my hips about every 10 to 20 minutes. I managed to doze through it, still not knowing whether this was the start of my labour. By about 5 am I had a show. I felt really nervous, but thought I'd be better going back to bed and resting, rather than getting stuck into my contractions upright.

I got up at 9 am and phoned the midwife, as the contractions were coming every three minutes, although still very mild. I thought I might be one of the lucky ones and have a fairly pain-free birth. By the time the midwife arrived at 10.30 they had got a lot stronger and were coming every four minutes. I had a vaginal examination which didn't hurt, much to my surprise. Labour was confirmed and I was 3 cm dilated. I wandered round the flat trying to speed things up, squatting in between contractions. I did my deep abdominal breathing through each contraction.

I started worrying as they got stronger, so Ian insisted I got in the bath. Brilliant idea. I could cope so much better. I felt wonderful, in control, and looking forward to the birth of our child. I ate toast and honey several times, and drank lots of tea, fruit juice and water.

The midwife returned at 1.30 pm. The contractions were still every four minutes and she gave me another vaginal examination: 4½ cm. A little disappointing after all my hard work, but never mind, keep going, 'You're doing great!' everyone announced; 'I know I am', I kept on saying. Back to the bath.

The midwife came back at 3.30 with a student midwife. Ian put on some music of their taste, made sandwiches and coffee, and everyone came and sat in the bathroom chatting away.

The contractions were now every two minutes and getting stronger. I managed to keep breathing through them. By about 6 pm I asked Ian to order me a pizza. It arrived free of charge with everyone's best wishes. The midwives couldn't believe my appetite. The contractions were coming every two mouthfuls! By about 7 pm my mood was changing. I couldn't be bothered with conversation and decided I wanted to leave for the hospital. It took ages to get there, there was a football match on in town. I caused quite a lot of amusement swaying my hips, in the queues. I was far from amused. The contractions felt so much stronger and harder to keep on top of out of the bath.

When I arrived at the hospital I had another vaginal examination. The examinations got more painful because I was having contractions when she was doing it. Only 5½ cm dilated. Oh no! I decided to let them break my waters. I didn't know how much longer it was going to take to dilate fully, I wanted energy left for the harder part of the labour.

Oh boy! nobody told me to prepare myself for really, really stronger contractions. I nearly flew through the ceiling, according to Ian my eyes were bulging out with the pain. I realized I was still laying on my back and muttered for them to get me on all fours over a bean bag. At that point I gave up. It seemed like I was a stranded whale continuously being washed against the rocks. I just couldn't find a way of getting on top of the pain, and thought to myself that I couldn't manage hours of this intensity. I was screaming and shaking with each contraction and everyone was shouting and holding me to get me under control. I was cross at the time, not that I could have communicated it, as I felt it helped me release the pain, but looking back on it, it was dangerous for me and the baby. I asked for Pethidine, an epidural, a Caesarian, I wanted the lot! Gas and air too!

They brought in a mobile Entonox unit, which didn't work properly. I remember looking around and there was about six midwives and Ian all having a suck on the mask to determine whether there was any gas going through. The ward sister came in with a shocked expression and said: 'Are you all trying to knock yourself out?' The next thing I remember was about two seconds in the lift, and then being in the delivery room. I couldn't be parted from the Entonox after that. I was still naked on all fours over the bean bag. I'm sure I was put in that position to stop me climbing up the wall! The gas and air was wonderful, I was so drunk.

Next thing I knew, my midwife had phoned in (on her day off), heard I was in labour and came straight in. I was so pleased, she's such a calm lady. I didn't actually get to look at her or say 'Hello', till I turned around and squatted for the delivery (the other midwives left when she arrived).

Ian was with me every minute, talking softly and soothing me with his hands. I found the contractions unbearable and tensed every muscle in my body to get through them. But at the end of it I knew I was going to be rewarded with a baby. The best thing I heard all day was when Ian said: 'Things are beginning to happen, they're putting on all their gear'. All of a sudden, I just decided to push. I tried a few times, not a lot happened. The midwife asked me if I'd like to stay in that position for the birth: 'No, I want to squat and watch the baby come out'.

The gas and air was taken away and I slowly came to. The room was dimly lit and very calm. I got really excited and waited for the pushing instructions. I tried and tried so many times (35 minutes) but just didn't seem to be able to get the baby out. After a while the midwife said I would need an episiotomy. I knew deep in my heart she was right. A few pushes later, the baby was on my tummy. The midwife had let me and Ian hold her as she was coming out. It made it so much more special. I was holding her so tight, that after a few minutes, she said to me, 'Shall we see what you've got?' 'Oh yes!' though it never seemed important. 'A girl!' She screamed once, but was very quiet after that and Ian was allowed to cut the cord.

I hadn't had the injection for expelling the placenta. I waited patiently, tried to breastfeed Amy, but she wouldn't suck. The contractions had stopped. I waited about half an hour for the placenta, trying to push it out, and in the end I decided I wanted the injection, I just wanted to be stitched up and left alone to enjoy the baby.

It was a wonderful birth, very calm and beautiful. I'd go through it all again, it's only for one day, and it's a pain you can't remember.

The drama of intense contractions close to full dilation are often described in oceanic terms – of rocks and shipwrecks and huge waves. It *is* hard to prepare for such massive sensations, as your intellect is not, at the time, able to detach itself and observe events. The pains themselves are all-engulfing and the only possibility is to dive through, breathing as steadily as you can manage. This act of surrender is hard for a generation of women who have defined themselves as people wishing to take control of their lives. It is without any sentiment of sanctimoniousness that I say that riding and enduring those stormy waves is an enriching and humbling experience.

Alana wanted a non-medicalized drug-free birth, but used Pethidine and Entonox. She shares her sense of helplessness and despair, as well as her eventual triumph . . .

ALANA

'It sounded as though they were all at the races'

According to Professor X (and he should know!) this was a textbook labour. No doubt a textbook labour in medical terms but nevertheless an overwhelming experience for me.

I had been hoping, as everyone probably does, that the baby would be early rather than late and by 12 February I was convinced I wouldn't have long to wait. Period-like pains had been occurring with increasing frequency over the past fortnight and the baby's head was well down.

The first signs that something was happening occurred during Saturday night when I had a few contractions through which I had to breathe deeply. I then fell asleep but by morning nothing more. However, throughout Sunday morning contractions were coming irregularly, most of which I breathed through and by midday I was leaning up against the wall and rocking through one or two. (The cats found this most distressing.) At 2 pm Tim came home and a friend came round; it was a beautiful day and we drove off to the seaside for a walk. I decided to announce to the party that contractions had been occurring all day but I wasn't too bothered by them.

The walk started fine with an occasional pause while I squatted and rocked my hips. As the walk progressed so did the contractions – every five minutes as regular as clockwork.

We stopped while I breathed and rocked in a forward bend – bending and straightening my legs. I found this really comfortable and was pleased with my improvization. I did notice though that I had to let the contraction completely go before I got up or the next would come more quickly and disrupt the pattern.

By the time we got in the car I was beginning to think this was really it. Back home, contractions were coming about once every four minutes and increasing in intensity. I knelt on the floor and rested my arms and head on the couch and hummed in between contractions to feel calm. We rang the labour ward at 6 pm but decided to stay at home as all was quite manageable. The midwifery sister advised I ate something before coming in as I'd had nothing since breakfast. I must say I'd never imagined myself stuffing down mouthfuls of cauliflower cheese in between contractions!

20.00 We decided to go to hospital. Contractions in the car a bit hard to cope with and I sing 'La' in between very loudly to cope and to calm me.

20.30 Arrive at hospital. Am put on a monitor and kneel with my bottom between my heels. Breathing deeply is OK for about 15 minutes. Again, a hum or sing in between helps, but I soon want to move around again. Midwife comes in and says the trace of my contractions isn't right – she'll have to run another 20 minutes. Oh my God! I can't bear being wired up any longer. Tim announces he thinks this is a false alarm (men seem to rely on technology more than instinct don't they!) After 10 more minutes I ring for midwife and refuse to stay still any longer.

21.30 Night shift takes over and I meet my midwife. She does a vaginal examination and tells me I'm 6 cm dilated with a soft stretchy cervix. She was the most wonderful person in the world when she announced that! (Other than for monitoring

> the baby's heartbeat, what is the point of that machine? Apparently it had been put on the wrong speed!)
>
> Low bed and bean bags arrive. We make ourselves comfortable and carry on managing for an hour or so. Then, I presume, we hit the beginnings of transition and I'm afraid I began to lose control.

Thinking back on all the classes I attended and the number of times we had thought about transition nothing can really prepare you for the intensity of it until you experience it. Perhaps I was being naive in thinking it was just another step up the ladder, but whatever, it came as an immense shock and one that I very nearly didn't cope with. As the first waves of really painful contractions came on I clamped the gas and air mask to my face and continued breathing deeply and rocking on all fours (my head and arms were buried in the pillows). The contractions became more intense and I felt the Entonox wasn't quite enough. I desperately tried to tell myself to breathe away the pain but I couldn't seem to let it go! I was getting very tired and very distraught and feeling like a failure. Tim was marvellous, telling me I was doing well and to make as much noise as I wanted; he kept blowing in my ear* and encouraged me to moan on the out-breaths. I couldn't relax in between contractions as I was so distraught by now – even though I had some decent breaks, three minutes or so. I began to say things like I couldn't go through with it and I'd do anything to be unconscious. I begged for help. Tim called in the midwife who suggested 50 mg of Pethidine and in it went – at 11.20 pm (prior to the labour I had sworn I wouldn't take Pethidine). I don't really remember it helping at all for this last part of transition but it certainly came into its own for pushing. We had another hour of excruciating contractions and I really thought I would die. Eventually the midwife came and did a vaginal examination. I was there but for an anterior lip. She broke my waters for me; she had left them earlier as she thought I was coping well at my own pace.

At 9½ cm she tried to pull the last piece of cervix back but I screamed at her to stop. I think she told me off and said I'd frighten the other women. She left us again to overcome the last few contractions.

Oh God! Again theory is not like reality is it? I started the contractions with big breaths of Entonox. Halfway through dropping the mask and rising up on my knees and then falling down again into huff-huff blows – only they were not the huff-huff blows we had practised, they were very very half-hearted and ended in sobs and 'No

* To remind her to exhale fully and avoid gasping and 'panic breathing'.

No's'. Tim seemed to be doing them correctly. I think there were only four contractions like that when I eventually rose up and said I can't, I can't, I must push (time about 12.45).

The midwife came and calmly asked what position I'd like to adopt. All pretensions at getting up on my knees or squatting had gone. I remained with my face buried in the pillow in an all fours position and to hell with what I looked like.

I had thought pushing would be a relief, and in a way it was – it certainly wasn't like those dreadful contractions, but it still hurt. My first attempt at a push by my own admittance was pathetic. 'That won't do', said the midwife in a very matronly way, 'you've really got to push!' So push I did, and my goodness it hurt! I remember at one point her saying: 'Come on, let's get this baby round the bend'.* Despite being familiar with the term all I could think was 'Hasn't it got that far yet?!' Eventually we got there and the midwife was very encouraging – as was everyone in the room. I gripped Tim's hand very tightly and he kept saying: 'Push! Push.' I wonder what it's like to be in that position, it sounded as though they were all at the races.

And so, on a big fourth push, Bridget's head slowly – and thankfully, gently – emerged with the midwife asking for pushes and pants and obviously holding onto my perineum. Cries of delight as I rested and then we pushed and panted out the shoulders. The midwife was wonderful and I concentrated really well on her instructions (just like our practises) and succeeded with her help in delivering my baby with just a slight graze; I shall be forever grateful. The most surprising sensation was not the crowning of the head (which was far less painful than I expected) but the slithering out of the rest of the body.

At last I could turn over and receive my baby, and was greeted with 'It's nice to see her face instead of her bottom!' I think the first thing I said to Bridget was that she would be an only-child but I'm already changing my mind.

All in all it was a tremendous, positive and rewarding experience and I am very glad to have been through it. Antenatal yoga classes certainly helped me to reach transition in full control and to be very aware. I suppose for transition you really need something to hold onto and I couldn't find anything at the time. Maybe next time I shall ride that part of the storm too.

* Round the angle between uterus and vagina which makes human (as opposed to animal) birth so tough.

Portia is another pregnant midwife. She wants a drug-free birth but is ready to be flexible. She gives birth in the hospital she works in – among friends!

PORTIA

'Was this the real thing this time?'

05.30 Oh no! not another trip to spend a penny – I'm really fed up with this every one and a half hours. However, this wasn't just my bladder again, I had a fairly strong contraction. It was strong enough that I had to slip into my abdominal breathing – glad I'd practised it. The contractions were coming every 10 minutes – was this the real thing this time? (I had been having regular contractions for up to six hours most days for the last two weeks and had even had a false alarm trip to the hospital at the weekend.)

05.45 Derek woke up and heard the heavy breathing. We laid in bed trying to decide whether he should go to work or not.

06.45 Contractions still every 10 minutes; decided to get up and see what happens. Derek decided to ring work and say he might not be in.

07.00 By the time I had washed and dressed the contractions were every five minutes; much more painful; breathing no longer enough on its own. Now's the time to try out the first stage positions. The only one that helped me was sitting upright on a chair and rocking backwards and forwards. Made sure that Derek had breakfast; I couldn't manage more than a sip of tea.

07.30 Ring the GP unit to tell them what is happening; decide to go in. Our community midwife, Andrea, will meet me there. Scrape the ice off the car – typical, this is the first frost of the year! Thank goodness there isn't much traffic about; the journey doesn't take long but is very uncomfortable.

08.00 Arrive on the ward contracting every three to five minutes. I bet my cervix is only 1–2 cm dilated! I decided to let her do an ARM (artifical rupture of membrances – break my waters) – anything to speed things up and get it over with! The contractions immediately become more painful and more frequent – every two minutes. Thank heavens for Entonox, it really does help. Derek is wonderful, really supportive.

08.45 Move down to labour ward on the bed. Very high on Entonox but also aware that contractions bloody hurt. I remember complaining at some point that the classes hadn't told me how painful it would be but Derek assured me that they had!

10.00 Contracting every two minutes; desperate to push. Examination by Andrea shows I'm only 8 cm dilated. I don't think I can do this. I remember saying all the usual things: 'Take me home!'; 'I don't want this baby!'; 'I can't do it!' I even told the student midwife that under no circumstances should she ever have children – the pain was never worth it. Everything hurts; I don't know what to do; Derek continuing to be very supportive; couldn't manage without him. No way to tell anyone anything, trying hard not to push. Student midwife puts her hand on my tummy, it hurts and so I shove her away.

10.45 Getting to the stage where I really can't help pushing. They are checking the baby's heartbeat after every contraction. When the student does it she can't always find it straight away; I lie there worrying until she does get it – it's all right. The contractions are now much more expulsive but at least I get a longer break between them. There is now no way I can stop pushing, and Andrea, at last, says I can. I sit bolt upright against a bean bag and push. This is hard work and to begin with I am useless. Suddenly, I feel the baby's head begin to move downwards and although it is still hard work I feel that I am achieving something. Andrea tells Derek to come and look at the baby's head. I can't believe I'm nearly there but I can now feel the baby's head with my hand. Andrea is now telling me to pant and Derek is doing it with me and the baby's head is delivered really slowly. It doesn't feel like a grapefruit – more like an American football or a water melon. The baby's cord was tightly round its neck and so I had to keep panting whilst Andrea clamped and cut it.

11.03 Once this was done the rest of the baby was delivered up onto my tummy, and Andrea told Derek to look and see what it was. A BOY! (What a surprise, I was convinced throughout that 'he' was a 'she'.) He was blue and floppy from nearly hanging himself* but very alert. He soon recovered although he remained fairly cold for a few hours.

11.08 Placenta and membranes delivered easily by Andrea, 50 ml**

* i.e. his cord was round his neck

** This is a small blood loss. About 50–450 ml is considered within normal limits so long as the mother is well. More than that is termed a 'post partum haemorrhage'.

> blood loss. All much cleaner and less gory than Derek expected.

I needed a couple of stitches in a very small tear and Andrea did these straight away. I then breastfed John and he took to it like a duck to water. Derek and I were immediately besotted with our son and couldn't stop looking at him and touching him. The surge of love I felt for him took me completely by surprise, I hadn't expected it to be so powerful. By this time I had completely changed my mind about not wanting the baby and was even saying that I would like him to have a brother or sister in a couple of years. I don't think that I will ever forget the pain of childbirth but it became insignificant once he was in my arms.

~

It is worth noticing how often women say that pain is appalling at the time but well worth it once the baby is in your arms. I know from experience that trying to visualize the baby during transition is no use at all. The phrases recurring mantra-like in my head at those times have been rather grim – things like: 'The only way out of this is through it', and 'Breathe in strength, breathe away fear'. I remember stray, weird thoughts such as: 'How could I ever have cared what happens at the dentist?' and also: 'I must remember *never* to put myself into this situation again'. I remember, too, the longing for oblivion and the astonishment that one body could contain so much explosive sensation. Even in labour, time cannot go backwards. Every minute you get through the dreadful bit is a minute closer to the wonderful part, the blissful calm after the storm.

The next few babies we turn to were delivered by forceps. There are two different kinds of forceps: one sort like a pair of spoons which lift the baby who is stuck at the entrance of the vagina out the last few inches into the world, and a different, longer kind, with a bend in them, to fit the bend in the vagina, which can bring down a baby who is stuck higher up, and can also turn a baby round whose head is in an awkward position. The idea of being invaded by metal instruments and having your baby yanked out of you is far from most women's idea of a pleasant birth experience – either for them or for the baby. As with all the other interventions we have talked about, the criteria and decisive points may vary from practitioner to practitioner, and this is where all the controversies are. However, forceps can be necessary and life-saving. Let us share some forceps deliveries. Sheila tells her story . . .

SHEILA

'I wanted to pack it in for the day . . .'

I had a busy day doing a variety of chores. Looking back I can see this was the pre-labour energy spurt people talk about, although women are traditionally supposed to feel the urge to spring clean cupboards (not my style!)

In the afternoon I went swimming, and while changing I saw I had had a show. I got dressed double quick, wondering if my waters might be about to break in spectacular fashion. I drove home and told Adam with some excitement that hopefully something was happening, and only a day after my due date! It was just before 6 pm.

Nothing much happened in the evening; I had no contractions, and we sat around wondering if something was going to happen. We went to bed at the usual time, and I put towels on the bed in case my waters went.

Thursday 24 November

01.10 I felt a whoosh and release of fluid, and knew that my waters had broken. I prodded Adam who was awake in about 10 seconds, and got working mopping up what seemed to be gallons of fluid. I felt calm but excited as I put the last few things into my case and defrosted the pack of sandwiches prepared for Adam to eat during the labour. I rang the labour ward who said I should come in as my waters had broken, but not to rush; I started to have some contractions at about 20-minute intervals; they weren't painful, although you were aware they were happening.

02.00 We had the classic night drive to the hospital, and arrived at the labour ward. The midwife gave me a vaginal examination which revealed I was ½-cm dilated – not a great surprise, as we knew we'd had to come in early because of the waters breaking. I was put on a fetal heart and contractions monitor for three quarters of an hour, and had minor contractions. My waters kept leaking out with every movement, and I went through the sanitary towels provided at a rate of knots!

04.00 The midwife reckoned that not much was happening and we were put in a side-room to sleep; it was thought that they would decide to induce me if labour hadn't commenced by 9 am.

04.30 I found my contractions were coming more regularly; they quickly got established to five-minute intervals. I coped with the first few in bed, lying on my side, and then decided to get up and move around, as they were quite fierce. I found I could cope without much difficulty, breathing and moving around. I watched the clock and timed the intervals between contractions. Adam tried to doze.

08.00 Another vaginal examination revealed I was 5–6 cm dilated. We were delighted – if we progressed this well, labour would be a doddle! Our midwife was encouraging, felt the baby would be here by lunchtime. We were left alone for much of the morning, and felt happy coping with the contractions ourselves. I moved around, swaying my hips and bending forward; I went onto the floor on all fours for some contractions and took some leaning into a chair. We had a tape recorder to listen to a selection of soothing music. We were also given a bean bag and rocking chair to use – the latter was marvellous, and not something I had thought of – it enabled me to conserve my strength during contractions, whilst still managing to keep moving. Adam rubbed the bottom of my back, which was also helpful.

11.30 Another vaginal examination showed I was 7 cm dilated. We were a bit disappointed that there hadn't been more progress. I was put back on the fetal heart and contractions monitor again, and confined to my back on the bed, which made the contractions more painful, and necessitated my using the gas and air a bit more (although I wasn't getting 'high' on it; just using it to take the edge off the top of the contractions). I found the contractions rose very steeply and quickly to a peak, and then died away, which meant that I didn't have enough time to build up the gas and air to combat the pain very effectively. Adam watched the contractions monitor and tried to predict when a contraction was starting, so that I could go on the gas and air.

14.00 Another vaginal examination showed I was 9 cm dilated, and the baby's arrival was predicted for 3–3.30 pm. I was in fairly continuous pain by now, trying to use the gas and air and sitting in the rocking chair to conserve my strength. The contractions seemed continuous and unrelenting – there seemed to be about 20 seconds between them which allowed me to take a sip of water or have my brow mopped. Adam was rubbing the base of my spine, which I found comforting and helpful. For a change I went on all fours onto the bean bag. From time to time I was put on the monitors. For a while I stayed attached to the monitors, leaning forward onto the bean bag which was propped up on the very high and narrow labour bed. Adam had to work hard to prevent me plus the bean bag crashing down onto the floor – a case of concussion would not have improved matters! I avoided lying on my back whenever possible, as the pain seemed much worse; no one could rub my back for me, and I stopped feeling any kind of control over the contractions. We started to feel dispirited.

15.30 Still no sign of the baby. I said many of the classic things people say in transition e.g.: 'This baby's never going to come', 'I don't want any more children', etc., etc. What I felt most of all was that I wanted to pack it in for the day and come back tomorrow to carry on. I was tired and fed up, and didn't feel I had the stamina to carry on much longer. I was struck powerfully by the fact that there was no way out – giving up and going home wasn't an option (I felt at the time that this was a very profound observation).

16.00 Another examination revealed I was still 9 cm dilated. It was suggested that I keep going for another two hours, and have another vaginal examination to assess progress at about 6 pm. At this, I flipped and said I couldn't stand any more and demanded an epidural. The sequence of events becomes confused here – I think the doctor was called at that point. Before he had arrived, the fetal heartbeat had dropped and meconium was found in my waters. I was completely unaware of this, as I was on the gas and air. The labour ward sister and a doctor arrived; we think they dilated the cervix to 10 cm and inserted a sonic heart monitor on the baby's head. Special Care Baby Unit was alerted, and a paediatrician contacted to be present when the baby eventually arrived, in case it needed resuscitation. The baby's heartbeat appeared to be stabilizing again. I was totally unaware that anything was wrong with the baby, and as I came down from the gas and air I was convinced that it had been born; I even asked whether it had arrived!

The doctor said the baby's head was in the birth canal, and I should start pushing; if the baby wasn't out in 15 minutes, they would have to use forceps. I felt no urge to push at all, and was just pleased that the pain of the first stage contractions had gone. I wanted to rest and relax, and felt quite peaceful. After a few attempts at pushing it was clear that we were getting nowhere – I had no idea what all this pushing down into your bottom meant! My legs were put in stirrups for the forceps.

The forceps were inserted and I was told to keep pushing while the obstetrician pulled. The baby was the wrong way round, and came down facing forwards rather than backwards, which didn't help its delivery. The sensation as it was pulled out was more terrifying than painful, and made me feel as if my insides were being pulled out. As the baby emerged and was whipped away by the paediatricians, Adam burst into tears. I was faintly surprised by all this – I felt too numb and tired to feel anything at all. I could see that the baby was a boy, and seemed to be sort of grey in colour. To me the baby was entirely academic, merely one part of what had become merely a medical procedure. I was thinking ahead to the next procedure – the stitching up – and wondering how much more prodding about I would have to put up with.

The paediatricians worked to resuscitate the baby – he was 'sucked', according to the notes – and Adam reported to me what he looked like, as the paediatricians completed their tasks and swaddled him in a white blanket. I watched in some amazement while the placenta was delivered; it seemed to take ages to come out, and the obstetrician and sister teased it slowly out, like pulling gently on a rope, and inspected it closely. I started to get cramp in my legs, which were still up in stirrups. The obstetrician put the necessary stitches in. Adam admired the baby and showed him to me. I still felt nothing, except that – objectively – he was a very pretty baby and not at all pink and blotchy!

The obstetrician tried to convince me that I had delivered the baby myself with only a little help from him – which was kind of him – but I had no illusions as to who had done the real work in actually delivering him, and just felt grateful that medical help had been on hand to get the baby out when it was needed. I didn't really feel that I had given birth to the baby, because I wasn't *compos mentis* at the time he emerged in the world, but I did feel I had laboured – and that I had been in control of the labour almost till the end. I had a good 'toolbag' of natural childbirth positions to use for the first stage, and an acceptance that medical intervention when needed didn't suggest failure. Hence I had no psychological hang-ups about having failed anyone!

When I was sewn up, I was released from the stirrups and given the baby to cuddle. The staff melted away and we had a cup of tea. I had a tepid bath, and we were able to ring close friends and relatives before I was taken up to the ward.

The detachment Sheila felt from her baby at the moment of birth did not last and they formed a very close breastfeeding relationship which lasted many months! It is exhausting even to read about, let alone to go through, these forceps deliveries, but it is important to understand these kinds of births as well as the easier(?) and more spontaneous ones. When strong interventions are made, the key all along is in how they are communicated and in what spirit they are done. If there is time and a genuine option it is important that an informed choice is facilitated. If it is an emergency it is important that everything is done as respectfully as possible within the limits of the emergency so that neither mother nor baby nor witnessing partners experience it as an assault.

Jane's delivery, though planned as a natural birth, included an epidural and forceps, but she felt comfortable with it all . . .

JANE

'Mike would have pushed her out for me if he could have done'

I had the first show at about 11 am on Sunday while I was listening to *The Archers*! We went out for lunch with my parents-in-law in the forest and I started feeling the first pains. I didn't say anything until after they had left our house at 4 pm and then shocked Mike exceedingly! We walked across to the shop to buy him lots of treats for hospital – far too many I thought – little did I know!!

We watched a video when we came back and I knitted – the pains were only every half hour then. By 1 am, with the dog taking an increasing interest in the interesting positions I was getting into every 10 minutes, I rang the hospital! A lovely calm reassuring voice said I was doing well and to hang on.

At 2 pm I rang again with them coming every five minutes and again I wasn't panicking so they told me to last as long as I could. At 3 pm the pains were much more severe so I told them I was coming in.

When I arrived they put us in room 3 with a low bed and rocking chair – very nice. I was given an internal and discovered to be 3 cm dilated – a long way to go!

Mike and I spent hours pacing the corridors with me hanging round his neck every time I had a contraction; he was marvellous. I had a bath and just kept on walking. The atmosphere was lightened by discovering Gill, a very good friend, had gone into labour the same night – even though she was due a month later. We talked together and then got on with the job in hand!

By midday the contractions were very severe and coming more frequently though very erratically. They gave me an internal at 12.30 pm and to our dismay I was only 6 cm dilated, only 1 cm more than four hours ago. I think that was my lowest ebb! I was told that I had protein in my urine and my energy was gradually being sapped. I agreed to go on a glucose and saline drip and it was suggested a drip to promote the contractions would be advisible.

No one pressurized me at any time and we were able to decide knowing all the pros and cons. It was obvious I couldn't carry on in the way I had, so we agreed to this. The tone of the birth immediately changed: I was given a high bed, put on the drips and had to stay next to or on the bed.

I coped for a while but the contractions became increasingly centred in my back and very difficult to get through in my exhaustion. However, throughout I *did not panic* and kept up my relaxed breathing – a triumph for the antenatal yoga which I'd practised!

Soon after this I decided upon an epidural (about 4 pm). There seemed no point in playing the martyr when it was getting me nowhere! The anaesthetist explained things very well and it was very easy; I had a top up one which meant I could experience the contractions without the pain. Then, of course I had to lie still on the bed with a monitor around my waist. By the end I was pretty fed up of the noise of Katie's heartbeat – reassuringly loud and strong! I was topped up twice – the only pain I had was incredible cramps under my ribs and of feeling and being sick at intervals. They were pretty sure she was back to my spine which is why, after all this, it was still taking ages.

At about 2.30 am Tuesday morning, I started to feel like pushing – thank God! Mike and the midwife stood either side of the bed and I put my feet on their hips and started to push down (they let the epidural wear off a bit).

I think Mike would have given birth for me if he could have done! I tried so hard to push her out, I think she wanted to come out through my spine! No real pain but where I got that extra burst of energy I will never know. After an hour the midwife told me I must think of forceps. By then I would have agreed to anything. I remember asking Mike if we could go home and also thinking and voicing several very uncharitable and unrepeatable thoughts about poor Katie!

The doctor was lovely, and explained gently that he had to first turn the baby and then get her out. They topped up the epidural and told me to wait and push when the doctor said to. The midwife had her hands on my stomach to check when I had a contraction. I had to push for 10 minutes then and she was out. I had to have a large episiotomy but did not feel a thing. Oh what a relief! She was whisked away because at the last minute she was distressed and released her bowels – who could blame her!! They cleaned her out, the paediatrician checked her over and then she was in my arms. Mike and I both cried and have been besotted ever since!!

Mike was so exhausted that while we waited to go up to the ward he dozed off on the bean bag in the corner of the room! We met three shifts of midwives and they were all, without exception, wonderful, warm and caring and made no derisory comments about natural birth whatsoever.

When I couldn't have a natural birth in the end I kept having to reassure them that it didn't matter as they were so disappointed for me! The midwife who saw me first eventually came back and helped deliver Katie and she was lovely. Even at the end, when the room was pretty packed – three midwives, three doctors – the atmosphere was reassuring and unflurried. Without Mike I could not have coped as well as I did: he was involved from the start to finish and I clung to him for support.

Without the breathing exercises I would have been absolutely lost and without the knowledge of everything that went on I would have been frightened. As it was, I coped, and Katie Ann is definitely worth it!

Sharon is a very young mother: she was 17 when her baby, Naomi, was born. I was 17 when my first child was born too, and remember vividly lying screaming at the ceiling in terror and loneliness as the pain overcame me and nobody had time (it was a particularly busy night) to even try to 'talk me down'. Anyone who believes in karma will understand the relief I felt when events came full circle and I was able to help another 17-year-old woman to prepare for birth. The delivery was not straightforward, but at least there was no fear there. The fact that baby Naomi was born on 14 April, which is my birthday too, made it feel even more symmetrical and peacefully karmic . . .

SHARON

'There was no pain at all after that'

Naomi was due on 1 April but did not arrive until 14 April. I was going to be induced the following week if nothing had happened by then. I was told there was a possibility of a Caesarian as she was not engaged at all, so I was pleased to be on my way by myself when I began to get contractions around noon on 13 April (although it rather messed up my boyfriend's 21st birthday on that day!)

The pain was very slight for most of that day, and I had a show at around 7 pm. I was *so* excited! I began to time the contractions but they were very irregular until midnight, when we phoned the hospital as they had been irregular for one and a half hours at seven minutes. We were all rather excited (my boyfrend, my mother and I), and wanting to get on with it, but were advised to stay at home until I was regular at about five minutes. I was rather disappointed, as I had to go to bed to cope with the increasing pain on my own, except for the help of those swinging hip exercises! I found that they helped enormously, and once I'd got the hang of them they stopped the pain completely.

By dawn I was exhausted, as I'd had a painful contraction every ten or so minutes for eight hours, so we telephoned the hospital, and although I was advised to stay at home again, I insisted on coming in first to be checked. I had originally wanted both my mother and my boyfriend to be at the birth, but when we arrived, only he was allowed in, so my mother went home again, although she told me she would be going every step of the way with me in her mind!

When I was examined I was found to be 4 cm dilated, but there was some confusion over what the midwives could feel bulging out of my cervix – whether it was the membranes or the blood vessels of the placenta. It was still thought that I might have a Caesarian, as the *four* people who had a feel (in the space of an hour!) couldn't decide what it was. (Naomi was born face upwards in the end, and this was apparently what they could feel.)

It was 11 am by the time I arrived, and my contractions had stopped for half an hour. There was a lot of waiting around, those first few hours, until my waters were broken artificially (I was very surprised at how hot they were!) and I was put on a drip to speed things up, at 2 pm.

(The hours between 11 am and 2 pm were mainly concerned with examinations and monitoring – I was on the machine constantly until nearly second stage. At one point I was held open with a speculum while a light was shone onto my cervix, to see what was going on, and Jack, my boyfriend, was shown Naomi's head.)

After 2 pm things began to get blurred, and I remember odd things but I don't really remember in what order they happened as the contractions began to really hurt, and I was given Pethidine – marvellous stuff! I almost instantly relaxed, and was able to sleep between contractions.

As the contractions were reaching their height, and I must have been nearing second stage, I was examined internally. I think the midwife was still unsure as to whether I needed a Caesarian or not. This was the most painful part of the whole thing, and I remember screaming madly and begging her to leave me alone. It seemed to last for ages. Actually, I remember yelling quite a lot of the time – more as a release of tension than anything else – and it certainly helped!

Somewhere along the line, a mask appeared from nowhere and I was given gas and air, but it really didn't seem to help at all, although Jack said later that he thought it calmed me down. I was also given an oxygen mask and my bladder was drained – a *really* weird feeling!! A lot of these things were done to me while I was asleep and I kept waking up to find different things going on that I didn't know about – which was the only criticism I would make about the Pethidine – I didn't really know what was going on, which was rather frightening at times.

I never felt the urge to push myself, but I was told to push like mad whenever I felt a contraction, and it turned out to be the best pain relief all day, although hard work! The pushing only seemed to last for a couple of minutes at the most, until somebody said the word 'forceps', and all these people started rushing around. The next thing I knew, my feet were put into stirrups and the doctor was yanking what felt like a boulder from between my legs! I thought I was going to explode, or the baby would be stuck there forever, it felt so enormous. And then, all of a sudden, all the pain and terrible bursting feeling was gone, somebody shouted: 'It's a girl!' (although I was so out of it, I didn't even think to ask), and this wet, heavy blob (8 lbs 10½ oz) was put onto my chest and I knew it was all over! (she was born at 5.36 pm).

There was no pain at all after that. Not even with the birth of the placenta, and it seemed within five minutes I was all stitched up and the three of us were alone. Naomi didn't cry once!

Apparently I'd had forceps because of 'fetal distress in second stage', but she was fine once she emerged. The classes prepared me mentally and physically for this experience, especially those 'swinging hip' exercises, which really got me through the night!

Monica had what can only be described as a ghastly labour. You will wince as you read it. However, even all this discomfort, pain, intervention, and complication, does not remove the wonder and joy at last. This is what happened . . .

MONICA

'I wouldn't have cared if it had been the whole British Army'

Wednesday 26

Now 12 days overdue. Had my show on Monday and have been having contractions regularly since last week. 'Alf', as my baby is known, is still far too high and I have been told that a GP unit delivery is now definitely out of the question. 'Alf' is a big baby, according to a late scan, probably over 4 kg, and I have a small pelvis with a flat sacrum. There is a distinct possibility that a Caesarian section might be needed, although I cannot get anyone to commit themselves to just how likely that might be. I am feeling really fed up: everything is going wrong, so much for all my careful preparation to attempt a natural birth with as little interference as possible. Everything I didn't want seems to be happening around me.

11.00 Contractions are now definitely getting more regular and stronger. Phone hospital, as instructed, and they say to come in right away, in view of possible complications.

15.00 Mike came home at lunchtime so we are now ready to go to hospital.

19.00 Have been monitored and examined and nothing significant is happening so I am to go up to the antenatal ward for the night.

Thursday 27

Feeling very tired as I didn't sleep at all last night. These contractions may not be achieving anything but they are uncomfortable enough to prevent me doing anything else. They have been regular at seven minutes apart since yesterday. No change all day, and baby still hasn't moved down.

Friday 28
Another sleepless night, so I am now absolutely exhausted. The pattern today begins exactly the same as yesterday.

15.00 I am sure these contractions are becoming more frequent. I hardly dare hope that something is finally happening.

17.00 Mike arrives to see if anything is now happening. I am quite sure the contractions are stronger and they are coming at about five minutes apart so he sits with me for a couple of hours to see if anything comes of it. By 7 pm we know something is finally happening so I send Mike to tell the midwife. I am now feeling very uncomfortable, but by walking about and doing a sort of belly dance I feel I am coping quite well.

22.00 A midwife finally arrives to check on me. Monitoring me discloses that my contractions are now less than three minutes apart and look very promising so the midwife examines me vaginally and discovers I am already 5 cm dilated. Wonderful! That really cheered me up because I felt I had really been managing to cope with the discomfort and I am already half way so I feel sure I can handle the rest. Baby, however, has not yet moved down at all, so that is still a worry.

23.00 We go back down to labour ward where I continue with my exotic dancing until 3 am when I am re-examined. 6 cm. Oh no! Another five hours of great discomfort have passed and I have hardly advanced at all. The monitor now tells us that my contractions are becoming quite ineffective, so a doctor arrives and breaks my waters in the hope that that will do the trick.

05.00 No more progress. I now have absolutely no energy left, and would like to just give up and go home. I am put on a drip to induce more activity and advised to have an epidural to cope with the extra pain this has brought. This will also prepare me for the possibility of a section, which is still on the cards. After the epidural is in place I feel much better. I can still feel the contractions, but the pain is gone. Although I cannot sleep, this does give me a couple of restful hours.

09.00 The epidural is wearing off and I feel very uncomfortable again. I am now, of course, flat on my back with a drip in my right arm and permanently attached to the monitor, so I cannot move around or do anything to ease the pain. I am re-examined and I could have wept when they said I had made no progress. The drip is increased again and my epidural 'topped up'.

11.00 The pain is incredible and I feel I cannot bear it. I don't understand why the epidural is no longer helping. The drip is increased again as I am still not progressing, and the midwife says she will call the anaesthetist back to find out why my epidural is not helping.

12.00 I am informed that the anaesthetist is now in theatre and cannot come. I am now making a lot of noise. The pain is worse than anything I could ever have imagined, and I am so tired. I yell at Mike: 'Where *are* they?! Make them *do* something!'.

13.30 I am weeping with the pain in my back and lower abdomen – which is constant, giving me not even a moment's reprieve. The anaesthetist returns and we discover that the epidural has fallen out of my back so the 'top up' I had was totally ineffective. It seems to take forever to get a new tube in place, mostly because I am in such pain I find it impossible to hold still long enough. However, with Mike holding on to me, we finally manage. The relief is almost immediate, but short-lived as I am now extremely sick which prevents me relaxing at all. Now that I am more comfortable again, I am re-examined and we discover I am 10 cm dilated, but we will have to wait until the epidural begins to wear off before I can do anything. Baby is still very high.

15.00 The epidural is beginning to wear off so the midwife returns with a student, and I begin to push.

16.00 I have been pushing for an hour and nothing is happening. I am very uncomfortable again, and feel there is no way I can go on. The registrar is called for advice and he decides to try and deliver the baby by forceps. The anaesthetist also returns and 'tops up' my epidural again. I am still very sick. I am flat on my back with my feet in the air (not what I had planned). I have a midwife, a student midwife, a nurse, the registrar, the anaesthetist and a paediatrician in with me now, but I wouldn't have cared if it had been the whole British Army, I just wanted it over. An episiotomy is performed and the registrar begins to pull baby. He cuts me again, and pulls some more. I am really hanging on to Mike's arm for support. He looks as though he wants to go and help the registrar pull. The whole room is a mess, my impression is that there is blood everywhere and I am losing heart fast. It looks as though the registrar is not getting anywhere.

They tell me to push now for all I'm worth. I don't know where I find the strength, but somehow I manage.

17.14 Saturday
Success! he has the baby out and next moment the paediatrician has her; a little girl. The whole room seems to spring into action all centred around my baby. Hours seem to pass, but it is only moments and then someone says: 'She's OK; she's absolutely fine'. The relief is indescribable. I am in tears, Mike is in tears, and a few moments later she is in my arms. I have never felt like this before. It is amazing.

I have to add that no matter how bad things seemed at the time, the hospital staff were marvellous and really made me feel that I am the most important person in the world.

The sheer length of some labours combined with one or two other factors (big baby/small pelvis, for example) can leave mother and baby with little strength for the final inches of the journey of birth. Let us join one more 'assisted delivery' this time a Ventouse* rather than forceps is used with Catherine, whose first child is due in two weeks time . . .

CATHERINE

'I'll have 18 months' break before/if I do it again!'

The weekend was spent visiting and doing usual chores. Andrew (my partner) had been up until 6 am Sunday morning watching the cricket. We went to bed about 11.30 pm Sunday evening. Later that night the 'fun' began.

At 2.15 am Monday I woke up and dashed to the loo, I quickly realized this was no ordinary pee! Fluid was continually trickling down my legs. I came into the bedroom and woke Andrew and told him my waters had burst. He looked very sleepy and told me to ring the hospital, he had no intention of getting up yet. I stood there removing pad after pad, laughing at this bizarre situation. Eventually I managed to gather myself together and ring the hospital. I was told to make my way there within the next hour. I was asked if I'd noticed any blood, and I hadn't. When I got back upstairs Andrew was still in bed,

* A cap is attached to the baby's head by a gradual build-up of suction and then traction is applied to assist the birth.

looking decidedly sleepy and not quite ready to get up. In between changing pads I noticed some blood on one of them. I tried to get dressed as quickly as I could and started to gather together all my things. My suitcase had been packed for weeks.

We arrived at the hospital about quarter to four in the morning, and were led to the labour ward. We were put into a room with an ordinary bed. A very tired looking midwife came in and got me strapped to the monitor. I found it uncomfortable being attached to this for 20 minutes. Afterwards we enquired about the low bed; we were politely told off for not mentioning it sooner. But a room with the low bed was vacant and we moved in. This was much better! There was the bean bag, rocking chair and a small rug on the floor. By this time I was already 5 cm dilated. Oh goody, I thought, it's downhill all the way from here . . . !

Most of the next few hours were spent in the rocking chair, or just moving about, swaying, holding onto the bed or on to Andrew. As yet my contractions were about every five to ten minutes and quite bearable. Breathing through them was easy.

7 am: shift change. The tired midwife popped in to say she was off. We said: 'Cheerio!' and 'Enjoy your sleep!', she certainly needed it, they'd had a heavy night apparently. We were very lucky, I think, that despite the shift changes all the midwives were friendly and helpful. The next two were with us from 7 am to 4 pm. It was a midwife and a student midwife. The midwife – Laurel – was one of these 'radical midwives', we recognized her, as she came to one of our parentcraft classes. The student – Pat – stayed with us until 4.30 pm; she was keen to stay until the end!

At this stage I was still cheerful and coping well. Both women were impressed with my breathing. Andrew helped by breathing with me, although some of his breaths were longer than mine and I remember telling him off about this! By the end of the morning I was 9 cm dilated but they discovered that the lip of the cervix was in the way. Once that was cleared the head could descend. The contractions were now more frequent, every three to five minutes. I remember having an enema to clear my bowels, a strange but not terrible experience. Early afternoon came, and I started to flag: I was still only 9 to 10 cm dilated, the contractions were steadily increasing, but my patience with the experience wearing. As well as this I was running out of energy. Horror of horrors, it was explained to me that because of my condition, I would have to have a drip to revive me plus a drip with hormones to stimulate contractions and also that the monitor would be attached again. The first time the lady doctor inserted the drip in my left arm, it didn't take and my arm went up like a rocket. So they tried the right arm – this was OK, progress.

I was now restricted to the bed. I had the bean bag and pillows to support me and sat cross-legged for a while. Andrew held my hand, breathing with me and advising me of the advent of the contractions by watching the monitor. Every now and again either he or Pat would massage my lower back which had started to ache. After a while, I was in the kneeling position resting on the bean bag. It was terrible moving between the positions as I was aching so much. Mostly I was sitting forward.

Late afternoon: my lower back ached, so did my belly, and I was starting to feel pressure in my passages. I felt terrible! And I told them so! Andrew said I was doing very well and the midwives agreed with him; they were impressed with my performance. I cried; I *wasn't*, I ached, and there was no sign of a pushing urge yet. I thought this would never end. I was beginning to get frightened.

I'm not sure of the exact time, but it must have been after 4 pm – third shift – another midwife (Cheryl) came in to help. I was starting to get what was the urge to push, although I wasn't clear about it then. Despite the preparation, when it came to the crunch I wasn't sure that this was the time. It was the worst sensation so far. Eventually I suppose, I must have begun to realize what was happening. First I was told not to push and then I was meant to be. I was becoming emotional, scared, I didn't want all the pain, all this hard work – I wanted it to end *now*!

For a while I had been using the Entonox but, by the time I had worked out how to use it, it was of no use. My breathing got me through. (I know it was explained to me how to use it, but that was under calmer circumstances. No matter how well prepared you thought you were, you rely awfully on the support around you.)

About 5 pm Cheryl said they would give me another half hour to see if I could push the baby out by myself. If, after that time, no progress was made, they would get the doctor to help. By this time that sounded wonderful to me, anything to get away from the agony. I pushed for all I was worth, it was damn hard work, but not hard enough. You don't really realize how hard you have to push at first. Looking back now, that part seems like a bad dream.

I had to be examined by a doctor so they could decide what to do. Compared to the midwives he was heavy-handed. It was decided that they would help the delivery along by performing 'Ventouse' suction and that I would have an episiotomy. I didn't mind: just anything to get it all over and done with!

There was debate about whether I would need to go onto an ordinary bed, but eventually the stirrups were rigged up on the low bed, and my legs were soon strung through them. I know it's not a nice position to be in for delivery, but I was extremely tired by this stage. The urge to push was getting stronger, I did a few pushes by myself but I don't know that it achieved much. Andrew encouraged me to use my breathing while I had the episiotomy. I still had to push hard. It was bloody hard work. I thought blindly that I'd been tricked; I thought that I wouldn't have to suffer all this pain.

After what seemed an eternity, I was told the head was out, and then the WHOLE BODY! It was a boy. I vaguely remember little blue feet. The cord was clamped and baby taken to the resuscitator, but they didn't use it as he picked up quickly enough. He weighed 8 lb 12 oz. They sucked the mucus out of him and he was handed to me wrapped in a towel. I held him while I expelled the afterbirth (injection again) and while they sewed me up. It took my attention away from these things. I think I was dumbfounded, shocked; it was finally over. Here was the baby. I think I was happy, I looked from baby to Andrew and back again. Baby was cleaned up and put into hospital clothes. Andrew held the baby while I was washed. I vaguely remember seeing a lump of red flesh – my placenta – on the trolley. After this, Andrew, baby and I were left alone together for about an hour. I don't know how 'natural' this birth was. There certainly was considerable medical intervention, but I don't regret any of it. Andrew was there all the way through, tired as he was, his support never let me down. I know I felt terrible inside, but he said I coped very well and this was consoling to me.

Later, in the following days on the ward, I found recovery easy, although my stitches *hurt*! I survived and both myself and baby were well enough to be discharged a day early – a few days after the birth!

Knowing and seeing our beautiful baby, it was worth while but I think I'll have at least 18 months break before/if I do it again!

The worst pain, the most horrendous experience is pushing! The prize is holding your baby when you come through!

5
Difficult Emotions

The birth stories we have read make it quite clear what an important and affecting experience childbirth is – both because it is the advent of a new life, and also because it is a huge consummation in itself. In our sensation-hungry and spiritually starved culture, it is easy to set birth up as a 'peak experience' from which we hope for a major revelatory life event as well as a healthy baby and an undamaged body. If one has done this, and then goes through a birth which is disappointing, even though mother and baby come through it physically well, there are difficult emotions to deal with: anger, confusion, regret.

Some women prepare conscientiously and carefully for a natural birth, only to find the pain is more than they can bear, or that there is clearly a genuine medical emergency, or a more confusing series of medical interventions which the woman may not believe were necessary. In these cases, too, resentment and unresolved anger can cloud what should be a supremely happy time with dark feelings.

In this chapter we will share some of the difficult feelings women have dealt with, after childbirth was – in some disturbing way – different from how they expected.

Margaret's first baby was born with ease – she felt proud and delighted and enjoyed the sense that she was 'good at' giving birth. When her second baby was born two years later, it was different . . .

MARGARET

'A case of wounded pride'

04.15 Waters go. 'Action stations!' at long last. Woke Neil to tell him. He had been installing central heating all week and thought I was referring to *his* plumbing not mine! No contractions yet so go to sleep.

07.15 Ring the hospital and am told to come in straight away. Still no contractions so decide to have breakfast while waiting for my Mum to arrive to look after Adrian.

08.30 Arrive at hospital. Still no contractions. Everybody delighted with the size of my 'lump'. Various guesses are made as to the size of the baby (suspect bets on the side) but it was going to be big. External examination only and it was decided that if my contractions hadn't started by midday they would start to induce.

09.30 After a time on the monitor (the baby was very mobile) and a long internal examination I was pronounced 5 cm dilated. Great! Still no contractions much to speak of. Wander about the corridors.

10.00 Ghastly pain in the base of spine. Felt as if the baby was trying to tunnel its way out. Heavy contractions, felt disorientated and legs were shaking. The dreaded transition I thought, my antenatal teacher had warned us about but which I had escaped last time. I had expected it to creep up on me but it was like walking into a brick wall. The sister came in and was very pleased, saying the baby should be born by 11 pm. Better and better!

11.00 'Don't you want to push?', I was repeatedly asked. The midwife called Peach was ready for a speedy delivery as the sister had said things could happen very quickly. Still 9 cm dilated.

12.00 Still 9 cm. Monitor on again. The baby was turning that much on his head the sound piece had to be held on by hand.

14.00 Still at 9 cm. The pain in my back is still intense with heavy contractions and I have had enough. Neil said later that the monitor showed the contractions in a series of uneven peaks, not at all like the steady rise and fall of my previous labour. I tried everything to cope – at one point I was furiously 'wagging my tail' giving the bean bag head butts and breathing the gas and air. Somewhere along the line I also started to scream as Nature seemed to take over. I kept upright all the time but the baby's head kept moving about and I was still 9 cm. At this point a doctor was brought in who used his hand to dilate me completely. This was very painful especially during the contractions and felt as if he was trying to pull the baby out. I merrily screamed my head off and tried to distract myself with the gas and air. I was told I was fully dilated and could push when I felt the urge. The sister in charge asked if I would like to start pushing anyway. I did, I had had enough! She said as the baby was so big I was going to need all the help I could get and to try and do what she said. I had full confidence in her and I was aware I was being taught on – this only being Midwife Peach's fifth delivery.

She sat me up in an upright position with my back into the bean bag and suggested I held on to my thighs while they held my legs at a comfortable angle. I pushed like a demented steam train, not trying to give birth but simply to expel the pain. After a couple of contractions the sister said I certainly knew how to push as I was already round the bend, which I found slightly amusing. The midwife and sister worked hard easing the head out through five or six contractions. I tried to ignore the incredible stretching sensations and just panted and pushed as instructed. The head out they waited for the shoulders to turn and then it took several contractions to ease them out and the torso which was also a tight bit.

14.41 Suddenly Neil was hugging me and saying we had a lovely boy. Neil was then allowed to go to the loo! Poor man; I had held on to him all the time and he helped by trying to get me to slow down my breathing and being encouraging and simply being there.

Richard was bright blue which the sister said was due to him coming through the pelvis quickly. I had a small tear which required a couple of stitches. I was rather jumpy about being stitched even though it wasn't painful after the area was numbed, so I got myself high on the gas and air. I was five miles high before the doctor realized what I was doing. The damn stuff hadn't helped with the contractions at all.

The young midwife was really proud of Richard and as other midwives dropped in to congratulate us she showed off her 9 lb delivery. I apologized to her for making a racket and she turned to me with eyes shining and said she didn't know what I meant, it had been a smashing delivery. I hope she retains her enthusiasm.

After a visit to the loo I had a bath. I have never enjoyed a bath as much, sheer luxury. Neil dropped in and said how well I looked and wasn't Richard lovely. I felt on top of the world. I was going to walk up to the ward but they insisted I was wheeled up in a bed.

After Neil left I got up and went in search of supplies and was sent back to bed again. I felt very fit and supple much to the amazement of the other mums.

That night I couldn't sleep. I kept going over the labour in my mind, why hadn't I coped better. At 1.30 am I went to the nursery, Richard was up and looked all fluffy and bright-eyed (isn't Mother Nature marvellous?!) – a beautiful baby. Why was I so annoyed? Later that night I faced the truth. I had been feeling rather smug about the labour. After my first one I thought it was something I could deal with. What I was suffering from was nothing more than a case of wounded pride. I had to laugh at myself. Then my antenatal yoga training set in and I found my pelvic floor still worked!

I fell asleep in time to be woken up!

Margaret's great good humour gets her through her bad feelings fairly quickly, and she shows that she is flexible emotionally as well as physically in accepting that no labour is like any other labour, even if it is the same woman going through it.

Liz writes frankly about the pain of birth, and her confusion that, as an NCT* teacher, she has taught women exercises to help cope with the pain and has certainly emphasized the point that a drug-free birth is preferable. It is important for all who are teaching labour preparation to stay in touch with just how painful childbirth is. As we have seen in previous chapters, Mother Nature has arranged for us to forget the pain within hours, if not minutes, of delivery. It is also important to be aware of the fine line between presenting options which counter some of the pressures from the hospital system, and starting to indoctrinate people . . .

LIZ

'A hellish experience'

If anyone likes to read of birth being a beautiful and sexual experience then they can stop reading here. This time, like last, I found it to be a hellish experience in which an overwhelmingly powerful force took over my body. The lesson I learned from the yoga class was to go with this force rather than stand aloof from it.

My labour was a long time coming. The baby was only five days late but in the fortnight before she was due I'd had at least two false alarms when I had bouts of regular but mild contractions for several hours. I thought things were really on the go when on Friday morning at about 3 am I woke with quite painful cramp-style contractions. These went on right through till mid-afternoon. I was further encouraged by the fact that my bowels were emptying quite frequently. However, apart from the bowels nothing else happened. I was up till 4 am the next

* National Childbirth Trust.

morning sitting on the loo! So when I woke again at 3 am on Sunday morning with cramp again I was extremely irritated – I was so desperate for a good night's sleep! So, rather than bobbing up and down to look at the clock as on previous occasions I just tried to ignore the whole thing. By the time I got up with Emma at 6.30 am the contractions were quite 'nippy'. I found that being upright eased the pain but increased their frequency. They were now coming every four minutes.

By about 8 am they were becoming pretty predominating, lasting for two minutes with two minutes in between and a few double peaks. I found that I needed Andrew's help to cope and I stood with my back against him, circling our hips in unison while he held my lower abdomen; very soothing. Emma was trying her best to help holding onto my leg and puffing out her breath noisily. But I began to get irritated with her and couldn't cope with her questions and demands between contractions. We decided it was time to go into hospital. I was torn between feelings of mild panic and disbelief that things were really on their way. By the time I had dithered about and we had deposited Emma at friends, it was 9 am before we arrived at the hospital.

I found the hospital staff very nice. By 9.25 I was on the monitor, the top belt didn't work very efficiently as I showed up only one contraction in the whole half hour I was on the machine. We rang for someone to come and take me off the machine just before 10 am. I think they had forgotten me. I was desperate to get up and move. I was feeling very down and tired. I was becoming anxious for them to examine me as I was in need of some encouragement. I also felt that if they told me that I was still a long way to go I'd need to ask for some form of pain relief because I had no reserves of stamina to tap.

Andrew nipped down to the car to collect something and I visited the loo. I was trying to remember to relax everything during contractions and I was beginning to feel that one of these times I was going to let go just a bit too much. It was while I was at the loo that I felt the first faint stirrings in my stomach (or roughly in that region) that I remember from last time as the so-called 'desire to push'. By the time Andrew came back I was feeling awful. There seemed to be no break between contractions. I suddenly began to feel nauseous, my legs were shaking, and I was cold. I know that all these are classic signs of being in transition but I also had another symptom – feeling terribly pessimistic. Since no one else was taking my labour seriously I wasn't either. Given the fact that first time round I had been in labour for 10 hours and when I felt I was in established labour I was only 3 cm dilated I was concerned that history might be repeating itself.

It was at this stage that the classes began to pay off. I began to listen to my own self. I looked at the bed and remembered the teacher saying that you reach a point where you just want to get up there and build a nest. This was just how I felt. So I lurched to the bed and got into a kneeling position lying across the pillows. There was nothing intellectual about it, it was all instinct from now on. I remember vaguely telling Andrew to: 'Get one of those buggers in here to examine me'. He rang and the parentcraft sister who happened to be on duty in the labour ward arrived. She and Andrew helped me through the next contraction. She had a beautiful soft voice which I remember as hearing in the distance telling me to relax and breathe. I don't know why but it's one of the things I clearly remember, just the strength her voice gave to me.

Anyway she hurried off to get the midwife. With the next contraction the vague stirrings down below erupted and my abdomen gave its first massive 'flip' which is how I experience the pushing reflex. As Andrew noted, the show rather than trickling down my leg in the traditional manner, shot out into the middle of the bed. At this point I indicated with a few four-letter words that he'd better call someone and let them know I wanted to push. The auxiliary who had earlier scuttled off to get some fresh incontinence pads for the bed arrived to witness the waters being shot out at a rapid rate of knots. I vaguely remember her leaving in a hurry and the room filling up with people scuttling around like mad. The midwife who had previously introduced herself to me in the corridor was telling the student midwife that she wouldn't be able to let her deliver this one after all! I think she said to me just to do like I felt but could she monitor the baby and could I manage to turn round onto my back while she examined me. I think at this point I took a couple of slugs of gas and air because I felt the contractions in this position 'rather uncomfortable'. She said 'Yes' I was fully dilated and could get into whatever delivery position I wanted to. I remember lying there feeling like a leaden lump and inertia creeping over me. Then I remembered last time when a similar thing had happened and the second stage had taken two hours.

I told myself that despite the fact that, like last time, the overwhelming force of what was happening to my body had made me lose contact with the fact that my baby could be born at the end of it, the other people around me were under no illusion and I had to hang onto their reality. I asked Andrew to help me back onto all fours and I collapsed onto the bean bag. Having been given permission to push as I wanted I let my body get on with it. I found that with each push I wanted to (or rather could not stop myself) groan and I felt that this helped me relax and push with my breath rather than, like last time when I stayed aloof and tried to verbalize my feelings, tightening up my perineum. I found that although I still did not 'enjoy' second stage I was coping with it a lot better. Andrew kept saying afterwards 'do you realize that you delivered on all fours?' and I had to stop and think 'Yes I did'. It just felt right. I had no feeling of pushing the wrong way it just felt as if I was pushing 'down'.

It probably took eight or so contractions to push the baby out. I think I used the gas and air a couple of times. Once was more in anticipation of pain as I remember last time I found it excruciating as the head was crowning and my perineum was stretched to capacity. The midwife at this point said that I had to tell her when I wanted to push next and I would have to pant as she was worried about the scar line of my last episiotomy. Then she told me to go ahead and push and she helped the head. There seemed to be a long gap till the next contractions and then the baby slithered out. This time I was much more aware of what was happening in my lower body. Last time it came as a complete shock when they handed me a baby. I had totally divorced myself from it all.

The midwife said that she couldn't hand me the baby though as the cord was too short. I was aware that they were having a bit of difficulty getting her to breathe. (Andrew had told me that it was another little girl.) I was unperturbed that I couldn't see her; I was quite glad to just rest on the bean bag, glad it was all over. Cutting the cord and admiring the baby I left to Andrew.

10 minutes or so later the midwife delivered the placenta. I had expressed a desire not to have Syntometrine. I had two small tears, one at the front and one along the old episiotomy line. While I was being stitched I totally indulged myself with the old gas and air almost sucking myself into oblivion twice; it was lovely.

Any afterthoughts? I still see birth as a brutal experience. I remember feeling shameful and guilty that I had presumed to be able to prepare other women for birth when I myself had forgotten the power and the pain of the experience. While for some people like myself to have as natural a birth as possible is a personal mountain to climb, I feel that to put this forward as the best way of birth for all women is wrong. There is no way that unless you are very lucky and have an easy birth that birth without pain relief can be done without a lot of strong motivation.

As last time I could not have coped without Andrew's presence. I understand that some people are now moving away from advocating the partner's presence at birth. For me this is taking the reversion to

Nature a bit too far. Their reasoning is that in the animal kingdom males do not attend birth but prowl around the perimeters guarding off predators. I feel that birth for me is such a painful experience that I need Andrew to be present – maybe as an anchor to reality. I also feel that since our relationship is so close it would make me feel slightly distant from him to go through such an experience without him having the smallest taste of it himself.

Following this account it is useful to remind ourselves that as recently as the 1920s it was put forward that women should not be allowed pain relief during labour at all because there was a clear Biblical statement that they should suffer (Gen. 21.16). It is an extraordinary paradox that regaining power in the birthplace at this end of the century has involved so much fighting to get the pain back. I think it has been necessary, but it is none the less remarkable.

These days it has become almost obligatory to take your partner with you to the labour ward. However, some men really do not want to go, and some women really do not feel as uninhibited as is needed for managing labour with their partner present. In many cases the woman may be living alone anyway.

Take time to think over who you would really prefer to be with you at this time. Do not be devastated if the baby's father does not want to come with you. Somebody who wants to be there and who can give you unconditional support for the duration of your labour may be a better choice of companion in the end.

Nicky's fast labour was rather daunting for her physically. It also meant she had no opportunity to settle in at the hospital, or to establish any rapport with the midwives. Consequently she did not feel at all co-operative during the second stage – the pushing phase of labour – and later was alarmed that this might adversely affect the baby . . .

NICKY

'No time to talk to the midwife'

22 September
Small amount of blood when I went to the loo. Told doctor and midwife; probably nothing, maybe the show!

26 September
Felt really well and active. Phoned Mum. She said often people are active the day before. What rubbish I thought!

27 September

08.00 Blood again when I went to the loo, but didn't believe anything happening, baby not due yet. Sent Colin to work. Went back to bed, couldn't sleep but no pains.

09.00 Is this a contraction? Made me get out of bed. Still don't believe it's happening but better get some rest just in case.

09.15 Must get to the loo. What, another pain? Shall I ring Colin? I'll ring the midwife to see if she thinks this is it. Midwife is not in until 11 am. I expect I'll be sure by then. Think I'll ring Colin but not until this pain has gone. Back to the loo. Breathing through it; wasn't so bad, sitting rocking on the loo!!

09.40 Struggle to answer phone: 'Yes I'm OK but I can't talk; I think things are happening'. Back to the loo, rocking and breathing.

09.50 Get through to Colin at second attempt. He'll be home by 10.30 am. Back to the loo, take the clock with me to time things and see how long until help arrives. Contractions painful but rocking on loo and breathing helps. Don't think I'm doing it right but whatever I'm doing makes it better. Whatever happened to the grumbly aches, pottering around and hot bath? Am I being a baby?

10.30 Colin returns; I'm still on the loo. Question: 'Is this it??' Answer: 'I don't know!!' 'Do you want me to run you a bath?' 'Ooh-arrghh' (sounds of deep breathing). Colin surprised by the amount of blood.

10.40 Discussed whether to ring hospital. Decided to ring, but don't leave me until after next contraction. Now pretty sure this *is* it.

10.50 Colin brings phone to loo and calls hospital. Too busy to speak, phone again in five minutes. More contractions.

11.00 Phoned again. Told them situation, contractions every four to six minutes. Hospital not interested. Call back when they are more regular (but how regular is regular?) Now starting to feel sick with contractions: 'Quick fetch me a bucket, but don't leave me!'

11.15 – 12.30 Contractions continue and now making a written list of times. Leaning over Colin's shoulder, him kneeling and me still sitting and rocking on loo. Colin suggests alternatives to the loo, but I'm not moving. Contractions now about every four minutes, range between two to five minutes, lasting about one minute. Still not regular but should we phone the hospital anyway?

12.30 Phone hospital. Still don't seem interested. Only agreed to me going in when Colin made it sound as though I was getting worried.

Most things were already in the car. It took Colin 40 minutes to get me off the loo and dressed. I was worried about blood getting on my clothes!! Journey took 10 to 15 minutes. First time I haven't worn a seat belt. About three contractions on the way and very trembly as we reached hospital car park.

Parking at hospital as horrific as usual. Found a small space but couldn't manage to open doors, manage somehow. Another contraction, used car bonnet instead of Colin's shoulders.

Which direction is the labour ward? Early arrival means we missed our guided tour. Got into main building where my obvious condition attracted the attention of a very helpful lady.

13.45 Sat in waiting room having more contractions. Half a dozen midwives poke heads around door. 'Are you pushing dear?' one asks. Then they all disappeared. Found me a delivery room very quickly where I was examined. NINE CENTIMETRES DILATED . . . What a relief! Not long to go now. I *wasn't* being a baby. Had my temperature etc. taken and put on monitor. Only one belt I'd expect two. Handed me the Entonox – what wonderful stuff.

14.30 Didn't get long on the gas. Had my waters broken and the pushing began. Most uncomfortable position. No way could I keep my hands behind my knees. In hindsight propped up with wedge, and my legs spread, was the wrong position for me, but there had been no time to think about it or discuss it with midwife. I don't even know her name and don't remember being told.

Pushing was not easy. 'Three pushes per contraction' – you must be joking! Could push once but when they told me to take a breath it just all disappeared. Anxious glances between midwives.

Midwives reminded us of a police interrogation team: one nice, and one nasty. I was being told off for not pushing properly. 'Now are you listening *very carefully* Nicky. This baby is very distressed and should have been born 20 minutes ago. It is very important . . .' etc. By this time I couldn't care less. Colin was doing more pushing than me. Had an episiotomy but hadn't noticed them doing it. Deep concern set in. Paediatrician and rescusc. trolley sent for. Colin better at getting me to push than midwives. Still took another 20 minutes, with head appearing one minute and disappearing the next – paediatrician looked very bored.

15.15 Eventually baby born. In the end it all happened very quickly. Cord cut and whisked off to trolley. Heard someone say Apgar score 6. Thought: 'My God! I have hurt the baby'. Seemingly only a few minutes later the baby was handed to me by the doctor. 'Everything is fine,' he said, 'might have a sore throat for a couple of days'. Took me three days to be convinced.

Looking back

Didn't seem to go through any prolonged aches and pains stage therefore didn't realize how advanced things were and so expected initial pain to get worse. Over phone, hospital didn't seem to appreciate how advanced things were either. If we'd been fobbed off on the second call, baby would have been born on the loo. Consequence was had no time to talk to midwife and so never felt at ease.

Think another time (but not just yet) I want to push either on all fours or in squatting position.

Spent first 24 hours at main hospital; staff nice and kind but very very busy. Went to small local unit, spent six days in totally relaxed and friendly atmosphere certainly recommend it to anyone.

~

Luckily, her baby *was* fine. He is a little boy, who weighed 6 lb 10 oz at birth. It really is hard in the throes of labour to get one's breath to say anything, let alone a complicated and possibly controversial sentence like: 'I'm not comfortable pushing in this position and I'd like to move'. As we have already seen an unexpectedly rapid labour can leave the woman (and the baby too) shocked and shaken. Fortunately, the relaxed and friendly care at the small unit was supportive for Nicky and her son who both flourished.

Danielle prepared carefully for the birth of her first child. She was fit and supple, conversant with the labour process, and well practised in breathing techniques. But she had a very hard time . . .

DANIELLE

'Little did I know what was in store for me'

Labour lasted approximately 15 hours, from the first contraction to his birth. I had Pethidine, an epidural, Ventouse (suction method of delivery), and an episiotomy.

26 April – My 'due date'

16.00 I felt my first contractions, whilst at a friend's house. I didn't recognize it as a contraction at first, it felt more like a 'wind' pain, and as it was accompanied by the need to go to the toilet, I felt that was probably what it was. However, over the next few hours, they came at fairly regular intervals of about 30 minutes. They were of a gripping nature, and I found myself unable to drive the car, or talk through them. They were also accompanied by diarrhoea and frequency of passing urine.

19.00 I had a show. My husband and I had our first real surge of excitement at this stage, but decided that it was probably best to try and quell our excitement, just in case it was a false alarm. I already had my bags packed so we knew that we were all ready when the time did come, so we settled down to try and relax and enjoy the rest of the evening. We had some friends around for a few hours and the phone never stopped ringing, with anxious relatives and friends asking if anything was happening, as today was my due day. So, despite having decided to 'play down' my suspected early labour, it was very difficult because of everyone else's excitement – it became rather infectious.

23.30 The contractions were still coming every seven to ten minutes, and were so strong they totally immobilized me. Hence, I was unable to move around, and had to just sit up supported with cushions, and concentrate totally on my breathing. Thank God for the breathing techniques – I would never have even got that far without them. I had decided to try and stay at home as long as possible, so was determined to stick it out for a few hours more.

27 April

01.30 By this time I felt I really couldn't take much more, the contractions were about every five minutes, so I rang the hospital. The midwife on duty suggested I take some paracetamol tablets, and see how it went. This I did, but by

02.00 I was in tears, and feeling distressed and that I was losing control. So my husband hurriedly made a few sandwiches whilst I rang the hospital and told them to expect us soon.

02.25 Arrived at the labour ward. I had mentioned my interest in a natural birth – little did I know what was in store for me! However, they started the routine admission procedure. I was in quite a lot of distress at this time, and felt very nauseated and was at the point of vomiting several times. I also still had diarrhoea. They put the fetal monitor on, and were not very happy with the baby's progress, so I had to have it left on for a while. This of course meant that I was on the bed just supported with a wedge and pillows. As it turned out this was the most comfortable position for me, and that was the way I stayed. The nurses and my husband were very supportive and encouraged me with my breathing; they could see I was distressed. However, immense disappointment descended when, following a vaginal examination I was pronounced only 2 cm dilated.

03.30 I promptly asked for some Pethidine, and this was given to me with some antiemetic drug (to stop that nausea). I had now been in labour for 12 hours and was only 2 cm dilated. I started to feel frightened and out of control at this stage. The staff and my husband were absolutely wonderful, and did and said all the right things. There is no doubt that that made a great difference to my coping.

From then on everything became a blur, the Pethidine soon took effect, and sedated me, but it did not even touch the pain, so although I was completely relaxed in between contractions (and the nausea had blissfully gone) the pain was tearing me apart. No amount of preparation physically and mentally could have prepared me for that pain; it was indescribable.

04.15 I decided to have an epidural, the Pethidine was not helping the pain at all.

The midwife did a vaginal examination and said I was still only 4 cm dilated. She initiated the epidural procedure, which involved breaking my waters, contacting the anaesthetist, setting up a drip, putting the scalp monitor on the baby, and a contraction monitor on me. This all took about one hour. During this time I was in agony and would not have been able to resist 'panic' breathing if my husband and the midwives hadn't been doing it with me and guiding me along.

05.30 One hour after being pronounced 4 cm dilated, and having had the epidural put in, another examination pronounces me 9 cm dilated – going on 10 cm. Little did I know that all that time I was in transition and that I didn't know it and neither did anyone else; no wonder the pain was so bad! I started to have the urge to push – in fact more than just the urge – my body just took over, it was the most primeval experience I have ever had. It was quite animal-like. All of this happened so quickly. I was very spaced-out with Pethidine; the epidural was taking effect, and then the pushing urges diminished considerably – which was a shame. (If only I had known I was through the worst of it, I would have hung on and not had the epidural.) But who would have known that within one hour I would go from 4 cm to 10 cm when it took 12 hours to get from 0 cm to 4 cm. Consequently, having had the epidural (which was wonderful in relieving the pain none the less, and I could still move my legs and co-operate quite a lot), I then had some difficulty pushing the baby out. This, coupled with some fetal distress meant that the baby had to be delivered by Ventouse – the suction method of delivery – rarely used, but much less traumatic than forceps. (The reason it is rarely used apparently is because not many doctors in this country have much experience with this method.) I was fortunate enough to have an African doctor attend me, who was wonderful and very experienced. I was allowed to push for about one hour – without artificial help. The midwives were all trying so hard to help me get the baby out naturally. Finally, they could no longer ignore the baby's distress and the doctor did a small episiotomy (my legs were up in stirrups at this stage) and with a combination of me pushing and the doctor gently pulling with the Ventouse, the baby was finally born at 7.07 am.

07.07 Baby was taken straight to the resuscitaire machine to be quickly checked over; he cried straight away. He was then handed over to me and my husband and we were left to discover the sex ourselves, which was rather nice.

The doctor very gently and quickly stitched me up, congratulated us both and left. A lovely man to whom we are both very grateful for delivering our distressed baby so sensitively and gently.

Although I felt the whole labour was a very traumatic experience – even a violent one – which left me quick shocked and distressed (as was my husband, who I'm sure felt every emotion along with me). I have to say the staff were marvellous from beginning to end. We could not have asked for better attendants. Despite the fact that everything I had hoped for went out of the window (except of course a beautiful healthy baby – the most important thing), the staff explained everything and asked my permission every step of the way. So they aimed to let me know I had choices and that even though it didn't feel like it at the time, I was in control to a point. So there is nothing more you can ask for, really.

Having written all this down, I feel a much better perspective of the whole thing. I did feel quite low and somehow inadequate afterwards, but now I realize that I did the best I could, and no one could do more than that.

I hope this account will be of use to someone.

I think it is an account that is of enormous use because it shows how labour can have many unexpected facets – twists, and turns, and changes of pace. No woman who wants pain relief should feel she is being either a coward or a traitor to any cause. It was unexpectedly all too much for Danielle and could for all sorts of reasons be unexpectedly too much for any of us. The kindness, empathy and respect of doctors and midwives clearly moderated the nightmarish aspects of this labour and Danielle's sense when thinking things through that the paramount hope – for a beautiful healthy baby – *had* been fulfilled, does bring things into a more positive perspective.

Sarah approached the birth of her second baby with trepidation, having had a traumatic delivery with her first. We finish this chapter with a birth which begins with difficult emotions of fear and dread, but ends on a very different note . . .

SARAH

'Everything seemed to go into slow motion'

My baby was due on 28 April, and on 27 April I felt 'strange', became very aware of the Braxton Hicks and was told by my mother that I'd probably 'go the week round', which angered me immensely as I had no intention of wasting another week. I had mentally prepared myself as best I could, practised my breathing and squatted all over the place in preparation. By Wednesday I reluctantly attended another antenatal I hadn't bargained for. The walk to the hospital set off strong Braxtons and the midwife spotted my dilemma and decided to do an internal there and then and declared things to be under way, adding that if things got a move on I could expect baby that night or the next day. Nothing happened! Thursday, the house didn't know what had hit it and I later went to Sainsbury's to get the shopping done 'just in case', explaining to Mum that if my waters went round Sainsbury's I was going to blame it on her! Braxton was back every 10 minutes. By the evening I was exhausted, gave up work and the contractions gave up on me – it was just Braxton hiccupping.

Friday I did nothing and was particularly foul-mouthed to all and sundry! Saturday and a housework blitz took place again and all the washing was taken care of. I went into town to buy summer clothes for my son and to Sainsbury's to get more shopping again – just in case! Unable to settle, I did all the mowing – I just had to get that baby moving. Convinced I wasn't really pregnant after all, I finally went to bed.

I felt anxious all night, hooligans outside had woken me up and I felt uneasy. Went to the loo and looked in on two empty bedrooms. My son's room empty (staying with father) and the baby's room – both empty, both soon to be filled. All night I woke and slept and spent pennies and slept and woke, and then dreamed of my grandmother who died years ago, and from that dream I woke with a twinge of pain around my bottom and under the 'lump'. It was 5.30 am. Five minutes later the same again, and again, and again. At 6.30 am I woke Geoff and told him I thought it was the real thing. Too uncomfortable to lay down any longer, I got up to shower.

Every five minutes the contractions came, but 'hours to go' I thought as I'd had no show, and as Robert was born 12 hours after the show, I imagined the same would happen this time. With an overwhelming urge to empty my bowels I abandoned the shower to do just that, and eventually managed something standing up. And so the shower/toilet routine continued for about an hour. By 8.30 am I had finished my shower and felt sick at Geoff's suggestion of breakfast but said yes to hot, very sweet tea, lots of sugar: no drips for me this time and I munched my way through some Dextrosol! The contractions were coming every three to four minutes. From the time I got up I never stopped moving and leant over something and rotated my hips or went down on all fours with each contraction – it helped a great deal. I was breathing at whatever level came naturally and which suited me best. All I wanted to do was empty my bowels and the feeling wasn't leaving me. I still had to dry my hair but was losing interest fast – contractions came every two to three minutes and Geoff was doing his nut. He was adamant about ringing labour ward but I told him I wasn't going in yet (I'd be hours yet – I hadn't had a show, I kept thinking). I began desperately thinking to myself that I couldn't hang on 'composed' for much longer; I so wanted to keep control and have my baby myself – I didn't want anybody to rob me of my baby with forceps; a natural birth meant everything to me this time. Sister suggested I was into a strong labour and advised Geoff to bring me in soon and informed me I didn't necessarily have to have a show! It suddenly occurred to me to go in pretty soon! It was 9.45 am and all I wanted to do was empty my bowels, and wouldn't leave the house for that reason as I had such a fear of 'messing' everywhere. After I'd managed some more and feeling quite desperate, I agreed to leave. It was 10.30 am. I could hardly walk to reception, the contractions were coming so regular. I made it to the day room where we were told to wait – to my horror, the room was full of expectant fathers and male staff and all the time I was contracting and 'quietly' breathing away. Suddenly I needed the loo – 'Oh God', I thought, 'I'm going to shit in front of all these men!!' The sheer horror of that idea forced me to the toilet block where, alone, I wept and felt terribly alone and desperately tried to go to the toilet but to no avail. I was frightened now and just wanted to get back to Geoff. Back to the day room; I was desperate and so was Geoff. I was just about to tell everyone to 'bugger off!' when sister arrived and announced I was going to have a baby. Either that or I'm going to shit everywhere I thought! Contracting every one to two minutes I got undressed and asked for a toilet – I needed to empty my bowels again. 'You probably don't', she said, 'it's probably your baby'. She's got that wrong I thought, she'll be sorry. I got onto the delivery table and lay back to be examined which made the pain far worse. 'Your waters are bulging', she said, 'I'll just pop them'. I didn't argue.

'I don't want this', I said. 'Don't want what?' she asked. Stupid question I thought. She looked surprised and declared me to be fully dilated and to push with the next contraction. Thank God, I thought. Everything seemed to go into slow motion. I was sitting virtually upright and Geoff supported my head as I began to bear down. But I couldn't add the effort of pushing to the force of the contraction and declared that I couldn't. The midwife promised if I pushed it would help the pain. So push I did, as hard as I could and to my amazement, it worked.

I could feel my body working, in control, bringing my baby forth.

It was incredible. I had never believed that I was capable of this and now it was happening. I pushed hard with every strength I had and suddenly the head was delivered. I looked down and saw her head born between my legs and felt her head with my hand. It was marvellous. No time to monitor baby, no drugs, drips, forceps or anything, just me totally aware of my baby's birth. Sister asked me if I wanted the baby delivered onto my tummy. I hesitated. I had decided previously that this was what I wanted but I felt so sick and I just heard myself saying: 'No'. And then I was pushing again and out she came. No one declared her sex – her legs flopped apart and I was the first to say: 'Oh Geoff, we've got a baby girl!'

And I just lay there unable to believe that I had undergone a natural birth. Something which, up until then, I had thought was impossible for me.

6
Other Complications

There are several hitches which can occur as the baby makes its descent into the world. In this chapter we hear from women whose babies took longer to be born or were born with more difficulty because they were not facing the easiest way for exit (face to mother's back, chin tucked in), or because they were breech (foot/bottom first). I have also included here two post-infertility babies, where everyone, parents and hospital staff, naturally are extra anxious, and a pair of twins, who also provoke extra considerations and needs. A woman in any of these groups going into labour will be watched extra carefully, and interventions may be considered more quickly because of the meticulous care the hospital wants to provide.

Helen's baby was a few days early and was hard to push out because his head was not flexed. She wrote about it *immediately* after the delivery . . .

HELEN

'I lay in a pool of blood and gunge, sweating and triumphant'

07.00 My husband gets up. I have a cup of tea after a good night's sleep. I feel some backache and general abdominal pain – like I have felt before so I am not unduly alarmed. I feel suddenly as if I have wet myself. Damn! I should have done more of those pelvic floor exercises.

07.45 I get up to put out the rubbish for the bin men – too late! Andrew goes to work. I wet myself again!!! Backache is now becoming quite uncomfortable. It's not too great but I have a sharp pain in the back with very little in the front about every 10 to 15 minutes. I was told that the baby was not back to back with me so I was not unduly alerted. I go to the loo again and feel a little plop and when I look in the loo I discover a small plug of mucus and it's streaked with blood. This, I knew, did not necessarily mean anything, but my suspicions were aroused. The dilemma I had was, had my waters broken? I did not want to go into hospital only to be sent home.

Andrew's mum was with us preparing to leave having stayed the week-end. She did not make matters easier by saying that I had not had a show – hers was a gush of blood! She reckoned that if you were in labour you really *knew* it!

10.00 When she left I consulted all my books and phoned Andrew who told me to phone the hospital. I did this and they told me to go in for a check-up. Andrew came home to find me on hands and knees on the floor, a position I maintained on the back seat of the car all the way there. My main worry at this stage was supposing they sent me home? What a fool I would feel and Andrew would have used up some of the measly two days' leave he was allowed for nothing. But what if they kept me in? The list that Andrew had written by the phone of questions and information about how I wanted a natural birth, low bed etc. might not get communicated.

When I got there they were dreadfully busy and we were put in a waiting room full of three dopey looking dads who watched with mild interest as I scrabbled about on my hands and knees waving my rear in the air which relieved the backache. We were eventually taken and I was examined: *very* unpleasant *but* I was 6 cm dilated – WOW! The hindwaters had broken but not the forewaters hence the trickle. They asked me if I wanted the forewaters broken and I said 'No'. They wheeled in a low bed when we mentioned it and gave me a bean bag but it did not seem worth trying to use the TENS machine at so late a stage. Contractions seemed to be coming thick and fast and I spent the time on all fours not swaying but with Andrew doing a lot of strong back rubbing.

I breathed deeply and moaned on the way out – as a relief. The staff left us for a while which was just as well as I did not want to talk to anyone. The senior student midwife who was with us most of the time was great. She encouraged me up into a squatting position but encouraged me on all fours too.

15.45 I was now having a lot of pain and I was offered pain relief. I tried gas and air but found it did very little for me, possibly because I did not like inhaling very deeply. The mask smelt terrible so I abandoned it. I said no to Pethidine but said I'd consider an epidural. The midwife examined me again and this was excruciatingly painful. She offered to break the forewaters which still had not gone and I said yes. She felt around my cervix and I had a contraction in the middle of it. I was 9 cm and it was too late for an epidural. I was given tremendous hope by this because I believed the second stage would be coming soon and would be quite short. I don't have a definite feeling of having gone through transition although I was sick but that was all. I thought that, before the birth, being an aggressive sort of person I would be telling every one to get lost – only in more explicit terms – but it didn't happen. The most offensive thing I said was 'Shut up!' to Andrew when he cracked a joke when I said that I thought my bum was going to explode. He was great, incidentally. I would have found it much harder to cope without him. He did all the right things and verbally did not fuss over me which would have driven me mad. Anyway, going back to my bum exploding, there I was waving it in the air and the pressure was incredible.

I had a reasonably long second stage. Alistair did not have his head turned the right way – he was chin up – and I think I was not pushing strongly enough. I somehow thought that a few pushes would get him out but two hours and 20 minutes later the two staff and Andrew were shouting encouragement and the head slid backwards and forwards. I was really tired but gradually I got the knack which seemed to go like this:

Contraction – deep breath.

Grasp the rail above the bed (I was doing a supported squat which deteriorated through tiredness into a semi-prone position).

Grit teeth – chin on chest.

Try and pretend you were expelling a grapefruit from the anus and expand the perineum at the same time. Who cares about embarrassing oneself at this stage? – let go!

'Do you want to feel its head?' I was asked. To my (now) shame it was the last bloody thing I wanted to do; I just wanted it out, out, out! A few primeval screams from me and the head came. I panted half-heartedly as instructed and the rest of his 8 lb 5¼ oz body shot out.

18.22 The cord was clamped and he rested on my belly. Episiotomy was not suggested but I had Syntometrine. The sooner I got rid of all the placenta the better. It slid out with a dull thud. What a magnificent piece of meat. I should have eaten it I know, with all those hormones, but I could not face it, even though I was starving.

Old 'big head' was wrapped up and put to my breast onto which he latched with a terrible ferocity. We were left alone for a while and then the senior student and midwife returned, weighed and dressed him. She said I had a slight tear and would have to be stitched. I lay there in a pool of blood and gunge sweating and triumphant. The stitching was awful although I can't say that it really hurt. I tensed my feet in the stirrups and held Andrew's hand. I chattered inanely. The early clean-up and local anaesthetic was genuinely the worst thing but I could feel or rather hear her snipping away and I had the strong impression that she was sewing up my vagina and rectum.

Andrew went home after that and I had a bath.

21.00 I dripped loads of blood everywhere. I was wheeled upstairs. I was STARVING. All they could offer me was some toast and tea but it tasted great. I don't think I will ever be able to sit down again! The nurse took Alistair away to check him over in the nursery and suggested they take him away for the night. At first I agreed but then I wanted him back. I felt so wide awake and I just wanted him there. Another nurse unpacked all my things, gave me some pain relief and an ice-pack for my nether regions which was WONDERFUL. I had another cup of tea and some biscuits – roll on breakfast! The thought of going to the loo terrified me.

It is now 00.50 and Alistair has been asleep for 50 minutes. Will I do as well?

Amanda's baby was slow in coming because he remained POP – persistent occiput posterior – i.e., with his spine to her spine, for much of the labour. He did eventually rotate spontanteously . . .

AMANDA

'I badly wanted to see the baby born'

'Finally the moment's come
And here we stand
All the words have gone

Along with all the plans
And though the hands
Are surely moving on the clock
For us, this moment
Time itself has stopped'.
Ralph McTell

This is the first verse of a song written and sung by Ralph McTell about two lovers parting at a railway station. The song was a sentimental favourite of ours because as students we were frequently saying 'Goodbye' on cold railway platforms. *Now* it will always remind me precisely of my feelings during the last part of the first stage of labour.

We actually had a recording of this song with us during the labour, as we had made a tape of our favourite songs to play during what we expected to be a long first stage of labour. With our three-year-old daughter's battery operated cassette player we were fully equipped for a concert – it was enormously helpful to us, a real ice-breaker with the staff.

I had really hoped for a spontaneous labour as our daughter was delivered after the membranes were ruptured because of reduced movement. But despite being 2 cm dilated and 80 per cent effaced when 10 days overdue, and despite two shows and lots of squatting I was admitted at 14 days overdue for the membranes to be ruptured again.

We arrived at 8 am and the membranes were ruptured at 9 am. From 9.30 am until about 10.30 am I noticed no difference in the contractions from those I had been feeling for about the last month. But from 10.30 am onwards they became gradually closer together and my back began to ache. As we walked around the corridors I just stopped to lean against the wall while Robert rubbed my back. But we soon discovered that leaning against a *hot radiator* was more effective. The sight of me wagging my hips against the radiators caused a few laughs but it really helped! We began timing contractions in 'radiators travelled' instead of minutes!

By about 1 pm the pain was shifting around to the front and the deep abdominal breathing – slowly at first and then faster ending with one or two deep breaths was very effective. By this time leaning forwards was the most comfortable position.

At 10.30 pm the sister examined me and said I was now 5 cm dilated. She said she had 'stirred me up,* to take an hour off the labour'! She

* i.e. ran her finger round inside the cervix to stimulate it further.

also said the baby would be born at 4.00 pm. This *seemed* an incredibly short time to wait and I was very excited. I was glad to get back on my feet, though – it was definitely more painful to be on my back. I knew I had enough confidence to experiment with positions.

From about 2.00 pm until 3.30 pm I sat in the armchair between contractions (now every two minutes) and stood on my toes with my knees bent, supporting myself on the arms of the chair for the actual contraction. The pain became lower and lower and very intense – impossible to massage. One midwife remarked to another that someone coming in now might think they were maltreating me instead of my actually choosing that position!

As the student midwife was going to deliver the baby I was sure that they wouldn't want the birth on the floor, so I decided to get onto the bed and leaned forwards on a bean bag, becoming more upright during contractions. By now the pain was indescribable although every alternate contraction was a little less intense. However, I was beginning to shout loudly and not breathe – or rather to exhale only. We switched off the tape recorder. The Ralph McTell song suddenly seemed too apt!

I was offered the gas and air. One voice (Sister M, I think) said she thought I had earned it. It was immediately effective in reducing the pain and enabling me to breathe normally again. I noticed, however, that some people in the room began to speak as though I wasn't there. So between contractions I kept butting in – just to remind them that I was fully aware of what was happening.

I heard sister suggest I might need some Pethidine after all and at this point my spirits sank very low. I went to yoga antenatal classes with the express intention of avoiding Pethidine unless the situation demanded it. The baby's presentation was not ideal – back to my back. Did the staff know something we didn't? Time really *did* seem to stop.

Unknown to me the student midwife and my husband were vigorously shaking their heads at one another. They began to encourage me in every possible way. It certainly does help to be told you are brave and loved very much at times like this. Especially if you don't feel either brave *or* lovable!

Apparently the intense pain and delay were due to the rotation of the baby's head in the cervix. But finally at about 3.55 pm I began to feel more pressure in my back passage and was asked how I wanted to position myself for the delivery. I badly wanted to see the baby born, so I turned around to a sitting position from all fours. This was more uncomfortable but now without the gas and air and with the need to push I knew it couldn't be long. The hands on the clock crept past 4 pm. I teased Sister M about her promise, but we both knew that the baby would soon arrive.

I felt the baby 'go round the bend' and with a little more effort the baby's head crowned. Now I could see why it hurt!

Next push and the head was delivered with the cord tightly round his neck. I panted madly through one or two contractions while the cord was clamped and then helped by the student, delivered Andrew into my own arms! FANTASTIC! Time – 4.16 pm; weight 9 lb 5¼ oz!

The baby and I were both alert and well. During the last few pushes I had nearly strangled Robert, but he was making a good recovery! We were so grateful for a safe delivery *and* the manner in which it was conducted. Not a cross word was uttered and there were many more laughs than groans.

Camilla's baby was facing upwards – spine to her spine and did *not* rotate before delivery . . .

CAMILLA

'Like a small jade Buddha'

My baby was due on 29 August and when I had a show two days early I became tremendously excited until a friend told me she'd had a show two *weeks* before her baby arrived. However, for a few days beforehand I'd had niggling little pains stealing across my lower abdomen – a sensation I once associated with an impending period. It seemed too much to ask, however, that my baby would be on time and I woke on the 29 August trying to convince myself that the niggling little pains were nothing more than Braxton Hicks contractions, which I'd had almost throughout my pregnancy. The pains more or less ceased during the afternoon, but increased during the early evening, as I had a drink with friends. I began to feel rather hot and uncomfortable and felt very self-conscious as people noticed me shifting around in my seat. At last I couldn't stand the attention any longer (my friends were getting very excited and I thought how embarrassing it would be if the baby was two weeks later after all!) and went home with Howard, my partner, feeling all the time restless and hyped-up.

The niggles were certainly more noticeable by now and by the time I admitted to Howard 'It *could* all start happening now', I had to sit down with each small sensation in my abdomen.

We ate supper and when I had to stop eating every few minutes I was convinced things were indeed on the move – and on the due date! At about 10.30 pm I had a hot bath and even though I felt sure I was in early labour I didn't actually believe it would be the last time I'd see my stomach that huge in the bath! I think the spasms/niggles became pretty regular then, about every 15 minutes. It seemed unnecessary to finish my packing – after all, I wasn't *sure* – so I got into bed with the intention of sleeping. Minutes later, however, I found myself in the all fours position, breathing deeply and slowly rocking my hips from side to side. This was a position I'd practised during pregnancy, but at the time it was the most natural, comfortable position to take – practise hadn't been all that necessary.

It was now impossible to sleep so I finished my packing, and Howard packed his camera, with the packets of biscuits and drinks I'd bought to take to the hospital (that was a joke – he certainly didn't have time, or inclination, to munch apricot and chocolate chip crunchie bars when things, later, started happening). Moving around was more comfortable than sitting or lying still and I helped Howard decide on which books to take to the hospital (so many fathers had told us: 'Take plenty of reading matter, it all gets rather boring' – another joke). Howard took a photograph of my huge, still stomach (the baby had been very still all evening) as by now I was convinced it would not be *in situ* tomorrow. Very soon after midnight we began to time the contractions, which were coming about every ten minutes by then. I either swayed my hips on all fours, or rested my arms on the bed and let my hips sag weightlessly. This was rather uncomfortable, so we piled the duvet on the bed and I crouched over that, slipping into the deep, steady breathing I had practised so hard throughout my pregnancy – a practice that paid off more than I ever expected.

By 12.30 am the contractions were coming about six minutes apart, and lasting about a minute each. My waters hadn't broken yet although there was some light bleeding, so I phoned the hospital for advice and reassurance. The midwife on duty said 'Stay at home if you're happy there, and phone us again when the contractions are coming every three minutes or so'. Suddenly, the night seemed to stretch ahead of me like an eternity, but every time I surfaced after a contraction Howard said: 'Well done, that's another one behind you'. The contractions weren't painful in a way that one normally experiences pain, they were more a gripping, invasive tension which could become quite debilitating. I began to eat glucose tablets in order to keep my strength up – I didn't want to be hooked up to a drip in the hospital through loss of energy.

Howard struggled to stay awake until 3 am when he slept for about 25 minutes. The contractions suddenly became much stronger. I began to scribble down the timing of the contractions on a pad, which took an enormous effort, and my writing was impossible to control, the contractions hurling the pen from one side of the pad to the other. The contractions completely submerged me by this time and I felt lonely and depressed as I thought of all the hours of darkness that lay ahead.

At 3.45 am the contractions became more intense and I could only exhale with a groan, like a great release of tension. Howard woke up and began to rub the base of my spine during each contraction, which was a great relief, until 4.15 am when the contractions seemed to be coming every three minutes. We phoned the hospital and they told us to get there when we could. Apart from anything else, I wanted to know how far dilated I was – if I was only 4 cm by the time I got to hospital, I was going for the most high-powered, hi-tech birth technology could offer! Between contractions I dressed, while Howard packed the car. I told him to drive carefully and to ignore me crawling up and down the back seat, breathing and groaning. Fortunately, the hospital is only five minutes from home, so I only had one severe contraction in the car.

Between contractions I undressed and put on a hospital gown, crouching over the bean bags and breathing heavily. A sister appeared then, went through my details, before asking me if I'd mind if they monitored the baby's heartbeat and my contractions. I was quite happy about this, but not happy that the monitors would, apparently, only stay in place if I was in an upright position, propped against bean bags. I was rather disappointed about this, and I'd been led to believe that the monitors would stay in place, whatever your position. However, in that situation it was difficult to argue. I just didn't want to be labelled a 'difficult' patient, and I thought I could tolerate the discomfort for 20 minutes, which was all, apparently, the time they needed. Unfortunately, however, the monitor wasn't working properly, so it all took a lot longer than 20 minutes. At the same time they did an internal, which I was quite happy about; by that time, the rest of life seemed to hang on how many cm dilated I was! The midwife broke my waters, examined me and said, sounding impressed: 'You're doing extremely well' – I was almost 9 cm dilated! So I felt pretty pleased with myself as I dived into the next contraction. It's all almost over, I thought. This time the joke was on me. The midwife offered me pain relief, which was the time to decide, and no later, as I'd soon want to start pushing.

Simultaneously, the contractions became much more intense as I became fully dilated and, I suppose, I went into transition. I decided that I could cope with only gas and air, particularly as they removed the monitors and let me crouch over the bean bags again. I don't know how long it took, but I think it was the worst time of my life as the contractions ripped through me and I submerged myself in the gas and air mask as if I could eat it! I was still controlling my breathing, exhaling so noisily that I thought the whole hospital must hear it. The pain racked my whole body, as if rats were running through my arms, legs and abdomen, eating me alive. The midwife examined me again, pushed back a small lip of cervix and told me I was fully dilated. Ah, I thought, I'll want to push in a minute, and then it'll all be over. But I didn't feel like pushing at all, which was a great disappointment – later explained.

The midwife put a monitor back on again, explaining how the baby's head would be pushed down the vagina, before slipping back a little reminding me that the second stage took time – and already I'd had enough! The midwife said: 'We want this baby born before 7.30 am, when we go off duty'. Howard told me it was 6 am and I arrogantly thought I'd be sitting up eating breakfast by 7.30. Laugh again. Although I didn't feel like pushing, it was obviously the time to do so. Holding my thighs, I bore down, which was much harder than I imagined – and I was beginning to feel pretty exhausted. I still clung to the gas and air, over-dosing on it so that my fingers and feet were numb and tingly and, once or twice, I slipped into blissful semiconsciousness. The second stage was much harder than I'd imagined it would be. It was hard to take a deep breath and push, release the breath and take another deep one instantly – all the time pushing with the same energy. And then someone said, 'It's got dark hair', which was incredibly encouraging; but the baby kept slipping back. This went on for some time.

I don't know how many journeys Howard made down the corridor to the cold water unit, as my mouth seemed continuously parched and my whole body ran with sweat. Throughout my labour, Howard was wonderful, my anchor and unwavering support. It must have been quite shaking to hear the normally controlled and restrained me bellowing and groaning like any primitive woman in her cave, but he remained unruffled throughout and, it seemed, quite unshockable!

But then, what seemed like hours later, I saw his face as he looked at the monitor: the baby's heartbeat seemed to be slowing down and speeding up with frightening irregularity. Apparently, the baby was becoming distressed and it was only when the midwife examined me again that everyone realized the baby was not in the supposed AP position but OP – facing up, and not down, therefore unable to get around the 'S' bend in the vagina. I was bitterly disappointed: after my speedy dilation and pretty efficient use of breathing, I was being thwarted at the last post – moreover, my energy was definitely running out. The midwife said they would call a doctor and, meanwhile, they transferred me to a high narrow bed, obviously because some sort of intervention was going to be necessary.

This was no easy feat as the second bed had to be negotiated into the room around the low bed, and I had to be transferred between contractions which were still ripping through me. By this time I'd reached the stage of saying to Howard with desperate intensity: 'I don't care how they get that baby out, but I want it out NOW!'

The position of the baby's head explained why I hadn't had the overwhelming urge to push I'd heard so much about – the head was pushing in the wrong direction, as well as shifting about trying to find the right position in which to descend. At some stage, the doctor had appeared, along with two medical students. He examined me and explained they would have to give me an episiotomy. This was something I'd been determined to avoid at all costs and, even in the midst of my trauma, I still felt mildly panic-stricken – one heard so many horror stories about botched jobs. However, it seemed I had absolutely no choice at all – the baby's head couldn't possibly squeeze out of the perineum in the position it was. (As it was, I was pleasantly surprised by the after-effects of the episiotomy – no pain, no difficulty in walking or going to the loo; within seven days I'd almost forgotten the cut!) My feet were lifted into stirrups – extremely uncomfortable, particularly when I got excruciating cramp in my left leg!

All this time, the midwife and student and Howard were supporting me, encouraging and applauding my efforts with each contraction. They never once seemed to give up hope that I was 'almost there' and issued regular bulletins on the colour of the baby's hair and how much more of it they could see with every push. Looking back now, I can only marvel that I pushed so hard for so long – I seemed to find reserves of energy I never knew I had.

At last the doctor said: 'If you don't get the baby out with the next contraction, I'm going to have to use forceps'. If I'd had the energy to speak I'd have said: 'Use forceps, I don't care!' but they were all so encouraging I *had* to have another go. Actually, I was given two or three extra contractions since the midwife and doctor had a small altercation as to where she (the midwife) would cut me.

The doctor wanted the cut to go straight back, while the midwife wanted the cut to go to the side. In the event, the midwife more or less had her way. The next contraction began to build up – my last chance. I held my thighs, took a deep breath and began to push, pushing harder. 'Nearly there', they said, 'don't stop now, take another breath! – push! – another breath! quickly, hold it! – push again! you've almost done it . . .' I don't know how, but I did hold my breath and push, release it, take another huge breath and push again, 'Just a little more!' said the midwife, 'another breath and push again!' Another breath?! that was asking for four in a row, and until then I'd only been capable of three – and those with difficulty. The sweat was pouring off me, but I exhaled and quickly inhaled again, bearing down as the contraction began to wash behind me. Somebody said, a long way away: 'The head's out!' Howard, who had been supporting me, looked down and saw a small face appear, still and composed, the colour of a small, jade Buddah. Elated, he told me: 'The head's out. You've done it!' Later – two weeks later – my health visitor (an ex-midwife herself) told me that she'd never known a baby in an OP position to have been pushed out by a first-time mother without the help of forceps or Ventouse. At the time, however, I didn't know that everyone was highly surprised! The midwife took my hand and guided it down, and the first thing I touched with my finger was a small, wet nose.

A kind of ecstatic exhaustion began to flood through me as I pushed with the next contraction – the easiest push of all. It was 8.30 am. Suddenly, all that mass in my stomach slithered out and, seconds later, a heavy, wet creature landed, all arms and legs on my chest. I couldn't open my eyes at first until Howard said: 'Open your eyes – look at the baby!' I did so, and found myself looking into the most beautiful, big blue eyes I'd ever seen in such a small face.

Anyone reading this who has had a baby will recognize the 'ecstatic exhaustion' which floods through you after the birth is complete. Camilla's baby is a little boy.

Jennifer's baby was lying in the breech position, and so would be born bottom rather than head first.* Jennifer was determined to try to let

* Views about delivery of breech babies vary widely. If your baby seems determined to be born bottom first discuss your options with a doctor at a hospital visit.

the birth happen as naturally as possible. Her doctor kept a close eye on progress. Three days before her due date the action started . . .

JENNIFER

'I was thinking, "Just try and stop me!" '

18 September

02.30 I woke up with a start as I felt something go pop and a flood of warm fluid went over the bed. 'Oh shit!' I uttered as I realized that it had started to happen.

Perhaps I had better explain that this: my first baby was lying in the breech position which had put an end to my planned home confinement, and since then I had been dreading the delivery as it meant hospital, plus being considered 'at risk' and all the technology and intervention that that would involve. I had, however, had a radiological assessment of my pelvis which showed it to be slightly larger than average and a scan of my baby at 37 weeks suggested that it was probably slightly smaller than average. The consultant had therefore agreed for me to have a trial labour and felt that I should be able to deliver vaginally. I had told him that I wasn't planning on having an epidural, which he didn't seem too concerned about, and that I didn't want continuous monitoring, which he *was* concerned about but duly recorded my wishes on my notes.

Anyway, to get back to the early morning hours of the 18 September – I started to feel very nervous. My husband leapt out of bed from a deep sleep and asked what he should do. I told him to do nothing except get dressed as we had to go straight in as my membranes had ruptured and there is a higher risk of a cord prolapse with a breech baby. I went downstairs and rang the hospital to say that I was coming in. The irony of the situation was that I had only left the hospital a few hours earlier as my midwife had taken the two of us for a conducted tour to try to dispel our fears; it had, in fact, increased mine.

03.05 I had my first contraction, just very mild backache which I wouldn't have noticed had I been asleep.

03.15 We arrived in the labour ward and I was surprised when the midwife examined me and said that I was 2 to 3 cm dilated and my cervix very thin. The registrar came to see me and said that he would like to monitor me for 20 to 30 minutes and if all appeared normal he would agree to intermittent monitoring only. At this point I asked about his views on breech deliveries and was relieved to hear that he no longer used forceps routinely even for first babies. If I delivered before noon he would deliver me.

03.45 The midwife brought the monitor in. She was slightly bolshy with me as I was making my wishes known. I told her I didn't want to be left on the monitor as I wanted to be able to move around during labour to which she retorted that once things really got going I would not want to move around and would be pleased to lie on the bed!

During the time I was monitored I was having mild backache about every five minutes which was quite bearable, but I found that by doing abdominal breathing the baby's heartbeat was steadier during and after a contraction. I ended up staying on the monitor sat up in bed for about half an hour as the staff were very busy. When the midwife came to take it off she said that the doctor had agreed to my being off it without seeing the trace.

04.45 Off the monitor. I got up and walked around. I went to the loo but found I couldn't go. My contractions immediately became stronger and only about two minutes apart. When they got too strong at about 5.30 am I did climb upon the bed to ease them a bit and my husband started massaging my lower back, buttocks and the tops of my thighs – this was the only thing that really helped. At this point I think he got quite concerned about whether he could keep it up as I needed massaging very hard every one to two minutes and it was hurting his hands and wrists. When the contraction started to ease I told him so that he could do it more lightly although I preferred it hard for the duration.

06.35 I was feeling a bit nauseous and the pressure down below was becoming unbearable during contractions. I asked my husband to get someone to come and give the Entonox. The sister came in and looked at me and told me she thought I would need some Pethidine, but that I could try the Entonox for a couple of contractions and if that wasn't enough she would come back and do a vaginal examination before giving me some Pethidine (otherwise my next examination wasn't due until 7.30 am). The next contraction started, I used the Entonox, the feeling of pressure was unbearable and I started to mess the bed. 'I think you had better get someone' I told my husband. The sister returned: 'Do you feel like pushing?' she asked. 'I think so', I replied. She examined me – 7 cm, another contraction, she examined me again – 9 cm! I think we had better get you to the delivery room she said (it was a special room used for complicated births). Another contraction – 'you are almost there' she said and after the next I was speedily transferred to the delivery suite. The doctor who had seen me on admission had gone off for some breakfast thinking that I wouldn't be ready for a while so he was called back. I had to have a drip put up, as a precaution, as I hadn't had an epidural so an emergency Caesarian would require a general anaesthetic.

My legs were put up in the lithotomy position but to be perfectly honest I don't think that if I had stood on my head anything would have stopped me giving birth. The urge to push was amazing, I didn't need to use any conscious effort at all. Everyone was saying: 'Good girl!' etc. and I was thinking: 'Just try and stop me'. Nature had taken over and nothing was going to stop it. My husband offered me his hand to grip but there was no strength there, it was all centered in one place, the rest of me was limp. The sister was dying to deliver me but unfortunately the doctor arrived as the baby's buttocks were appearing. They had a little fight at the end of the table but of course he won and informed me that it was routine to do an episiotomy – 'just in case'.

07.25 Rosalind was born just five hours after my membranes had ruptured and only two hours after I started experiencing any discomfort. She was in a good state of health scoring an Apgar of 9 at one minute. I was on cloud nine as I had fully expected at least a forceps delivery, and in actual fact I had almost done it all by myself – and probably would have done if a doctor hadn't been present.

Susanna sets the scene for the birth of her baby, after many years of waiting . . .

SUSANNA

'Well, at least I don't have to do any housework today!'

This is a report of a birth destined to be 'mechanical' from the outset due to the age of mother (40 last week!) to be expecting a first child and baby's size – deemed to be small at a calculated 6–6½ lbs.

Again, due to my age, my pregnancy was not allowed to continue beyond 40 weeks and I was admitted to the antenatal ward at 2.30 pm on 30 June to be induced on Monday morning. On admission I was monitored for half an hour and the staff quickly explained what would happen, hoping to come back for a longer chat later but they were very busy. My husband was allowed to stay until about 9 pm and then told to report to the delivery suite the next morning at 8 am. I shared a two-bedded room with a girl whose waters had broken. Neither of us could sleep as it was a stifling hot night; we couldn't open the window or work out how the backs of the beds lowered (next time I'd ask!) A doctor came and examined me at 12.40 am!! (thank goodness for relaxation exercises!) and inserted a pessary to soften the neck of the womb. About 6 am the sister came and checked me over. I jokingly complained that the baby had been lying most uncomfortably all night and she laughed – I'd been contracting without knowing it and was 2 cm and she didn't think I'd need to be induced; I was over the moon. My husband arrived before I went down to the delivery suite and we walked down together; he did carry my case! The first thing I heard in the delivery room was someone saying urgently: 'I want to push!' – lucky them, they were well on their way! It was a beautiful morning and I had a lovely room. I sat in the window watching a lady opposite cleaning her steps and thinking: 'Well at least I don't have to do any housework today!' The only problem at that stage was that I was starting labour with lack of sleep and emotions running high – feeling as if I'd been to an all-night party. The staff were all fantastic, considering the pressure they were working under. A sister kept poking her head round the door saying: 'I haven't forgotten you, Mrs Thatch, I've just got to have another baby'.

It was about 10 am when the nurses and doctor finally managed to come and examine and talk to me. The doctor gave both my husband and me the impression that he thought I'd have a Caesarian delivery and anything other than that would be a bonus. He also said the only form of pain relief he wanted to use was an epidural as Pethidine and gas and air would only make me more sleepy. He also didn't want me to have a long labour due to baby's size. I explained that I had been to natural birth classes but was entering my confinement with an open mind and would do anything I was advised to ensure baby was delivered safely. The doctor then examined me – still 2 cm. They decided the best course of action was to break my waters and induce me. Enter all the machinery and exit one husband looking extremely pale, but thereafter he was fine. A monitor was fixed to the baby's head and strapped round the top of my leg. Natural instinct made me want to bend over and move my hips during contractions and I asked if I could stand up and lean against the edge of the bed. I was told be it on my own head because if the strap round my leg moved the monitor might pull off the baby's head and I was the one that would have to put up with it being refitted but I was allowed to sit up in a chair. Guess what happened anyway? – the monitor came off (mind you it had been fitted by a doctor; once it had come off the midwife was allowed to refit it and it stayed on!) About midday they sent my husband home for more sandwiches as they reckoned it was going to be quite a long job. He returned bringing me an evening paper to read which I usually love but couldn't concentrate on that day. Although the contractions were quite regular they were not too severe and I could cope with deep breathing.

About 2.15 pm I had another examination – still 2 cm! – the doctor said that what they would like to do is give me an epidural so that they could bump the induction right up to get things moving and even so baby wouldn't be born until 10 pm, probably nearer 12 pm. While they were putting in the epidural I was having really nippy contractions but I was allowed to sit on the edge of the bed and lean over a pile of pillows. Instead of a break between contractions I was having a needle put in my back! Once the epidural was in I had to lie on the bed and complained that although the pains in front had gone, I still had pains underneath between my legs. After about 15 minutes I said I was sorry but I wouldn't be able to stand these pains for another eight hours. The doctor was recalled, he seemed to think the situation strange but mixed up some 'cocktail' and topped the epidural right up which made my legs go numb. The sister was doing another delivery and a student midwife had been sent in with me to 'babysit'. I complained to her that I still felt as if I wanted to push. She had a quick look at me and exclaimed to my husband: 'Come and look at this, do you think it's the baby's head?' 'Goodness!', thought I, 'they'll be asking him if he'd like to deliver it next!' She said she'd get the sister and they'd do another full examination as it could be something other than the head she could see (it was a technical term I didn't understand). I remember saying to her 'If I'm still 2 cm don't tell me'.

The atmosphere was quite electric when they examined me: I'd gone from 2 cm to 10 cm in half an hour!! I presume when they were putting the epidural in I must have near enough been in transition and imagine being told you're going to be in transition for at least eight hours!!!

They then decided to leave me for an hour to allow the epidural to wear off and baby to turn as he was lying with his back to my back. (I've since found out that the nurse told my husband that the machine wasn't registering the contractions properly – if only I'd said I wanted to push earlier and asked to be examined again!)

After about half an hour the sister returned and said 'This baby wants to come into the world and we're going to deliver it on our own'. Evidently any problems and I had to have a doctor to do the delivery. It sounds conceited but I had already made up my mind that I would be good at pushing but of course I had to be told when to push as I couldn't feel the contractions. I had to have a small episiotomy and I can remember hearing myself grunting as I pushed, although we'd been warned not to as it gives you a sore throat. Within about 20 minutes I was told to pant and with that he was there yelling his head off. I was saying to my husband: 'Take a picture', 'take a picture!' and wondering why they didn't give him straight to me but they were still working on me as I had a retained placenta.

My husband says he'd like to mention something here. He says all the warnings in the world could not have prepared him for the blueness of the baby and how his face changed to a lovely shade of pink as he cried.

As he was born my left breast oozed liquid and once he was wrapped he was given to me to feed before I went to theatre to have the placenta removed which was done with a spinal block so once it was out I was still 'with it'. My husband was literally left 'holding the baby' while I was in theatre – good for bonding?

To me, Joseph's birth was wonderful and now three months later, he's totally breastfed, over 13 lb and thriving and I've never been more tired or happier in all my life.

Sally had not just a long wait for her second child but several extra problems in between . . .

SALLY

'Someone says he has big feet . . .'

Our first child, now six, was breech. We have reasonably happy memories of a 'hi-tech' birth including forceps, episiotomy, stirrups, Pethidine and gas and air. The staff had been supportive and we were pleased to have delivered vaginally. She was born in an operating theatre in Aberdeen with many people present and ten trainee midwives sitting in a little gallery. My main disappointment was that the Pethidine meant that I could not remember some of the birth, but also I felt monitoring of the breech during labour was almost more painful than the contractions. The monitor kept dropping off her foot and more and more people had a go at putting it back on again.

I had an ectopic pregnancy five months later which meant I lost one tube. During the next four or five years I spent many hours sitting in the infertility clinic, had three minor operations, and consumed vast quantities of fertility drugs. It culminated in a tubal bypass operation which was my only chance of having another child – apart from *In-vitro* fertilization (IVF). I had to wait for a year for this.

So, I was delighted when I found out I was five months pregnant (the drugs had masked normal signs). Right from the beginning it was obvious they were going to keep a close eye on things. I saw the consultant on every visit to the hospital. I told him I wanted a natural birth. He said that if everything looked OK then I could certainly start labour and I would be closely monitored (the reason for the concern was that although my Fallopian tube had worked once it might not work again so I might never have another pregnancy).

As my due date approached my consultant announced that if I went one day over I would have a Caesarian. I was very upset by this and managed to negotiate three more days. I even made another appointment and took my husband for moral support. The outcome of this was that the consultant said I would have to sign a form absolving him of all responsibility if I went past my dates. We were not prepared to do this. It was a very worrying time. As each day passed I felt more and more desperate for my labour to start.

My birth report starts at 9 pm the night before I was due to report to the hospital at 9 am for the Caesarian section . . .

1.00 Odd period-like pains – ignore them.
3.00 Go to bed hoping for anything to happen.

00.30 Get 'period' pains every 15 minutes. I keep awake to make sure they keep on coming – I am very happy that they do.

02.15 Pains get slightly bigger so I go down for a cup of tea. I attempt to watch a video. The contractions get bigger so I stand leaning forward, wiggling hips and breathing. The contractions are quite short. In between I am normal. I go to pack Kate's clothes for school the next day. I lean over banisters as I have a contraction on the stairs.

03.30 Decide to tell Mark – I didn't want to raise his hopes before. He looks up and rolls over back to sleep.

03.40 Go back to Mark who is still sleeping. I swear very loudly at him! He gets up, and I insist he has a shower (apparently I insisted the same last time!)

03.50 Ring Christine who has a bed made up for Kate. She is walked round in her dressing gown. Contractions getting more painful but I am really mastering the art of hip swinging and breathing as learnt in my antenatal classes. I learn early on that I have to be ready and prepared at the start of each contraction. I feel in control and confident. I use this standing position the whole way through my labour.

I had always planned to save my bath as a luxury so now seemed like the time. I don't realize until I am in there that there is nothing to lean on in our bath. Have three contractions in bath. Get dressed, Mark comes back and puts bags in car. I am timing contractions and realize that I have had 45 minutes at less than five minutes apart. The odd one is much harder and longer. Christine rings up at 4 am and says, 'Haven't you gone yet?' I phone up the hospital and am thrown by the need to have a hospital number. I get a contraction and Mark has to take over.

I have a contraction in the street leaning over the car and crawl into the back seat of the Mini. The corners are the worst. Arrive at the underground car park of the hospital only to find the access door shut. We walk round. I have contractions on four or five cars on the way up the hill. It is a lovely night. I am delighted to think that I am beating my consultant's knife and hope there is nothing on my notes requesting special intervention.

I have a contraction on the reception desk. A nurse appears – I wonder if she is my midwife. I have two contractions over hot heaters in the corridor. We are shown into a room. We are just left alone for 10 minutes. I look for a place to wiggle on and choose an equipment trolley at the end of the bed. A gown appears. I put it on. When I lean forward to sway I get very cold so Mark's role is to hold the gown together. Between the contractions I am quite normal. I just stroll around the room. At the height of the contractions I feel very sick for five seconds so I have a sick bowl at my feet. I am not sick but can't control my temperature. Our midwife appears. I am reassured because she has a Geordie accent. She doesn't say much and leaves us alone. I thought she would check my cervix and monitor me for 20 minutes but she doesn't. She seems to know I am quite far on. I tell her that I am coping well if I stand. She says she will get the mobile monitor. Time seems to pass. The midwife is not around much which suits us. I say I would like my cervix checked. I manage to jump on the bed between contractions. She says I am ready. I want to open my bowels very badly. The midwife says it's the baby. I know it's not so I am allowed to go to the toilet. I do open my bowels and feel much better. When I stand up I get a huge powerful pushing contraction. I attempt to get into the breathing but I feel a great sense of panic because I am on my own and in a strange place. I do something I thought I'd never do: I pull the emergency cord. I am rescued by two nurses and my midwife. I am led back to my room. The midwife checks my cervix and says I can push. I feel another contraction coming. I roll off the bed and have it kneeling on the floor. My midwife is insistent for the first and only time; she says I cannot deliver on to the floor because she might not be able to catch the baby. I kneel over the end of the bed facing the wall. She uses the mobile monitor on my tummy which I find reassuring. The midwife tells me to push, I ask her what to do because I've forgotten. She says do what you think best and leaves it up to me. This approach really suits me. I have the first pushing contraction. I make a noise and attempt to push. It takes me three contractions to get the hang of it.

Apparently I keep asking Mark to rub my back but I do not remember this. The midwife tells me the baby may be in distress so I must push much more effectively. She tells me that if I am kneeling she won't be able to deliver on to my tummy. I tell her that I don't bloody care! On the fourth contraction I don't make any noise: I hold my breath, push and keep the push going. It is extremely hard work. I can feel the stretch. She says: 'Well done, feel the head'. I put my hand down but it has slipped back. A sister comes in to the room. I don't know this till later. Next push and the head is out. Mark tells me that there were a few doctors popping in and out. Because I am facing the wall I am unaware of this activity. There is meconium and the cord is around the baby's neck. The baby is aspirated by the paediatrician. I don't see him till later. With the fifth contraction I push the baby out. I make a VERY loud noise. I don't look round I am busy recovering. The first thing I hear is a murmur or gurgling. I am still too overwhelmed to turn round. Mark says it is a boy. My memory is a little blurred here I think a doctor looks at him near a machine in the corner. Someone says he has big feet. I turn round and sit on the bed. Neither Mark nor I can remember if I held Henry or not at this time.

The next thing that happened was something we were totally unprepared for. While the midwife was pulling out the placenta the cord snapped. My next memory is the midwife looking very worried. She tries to reach in and pull it out. The sister tells me to get really high on gas and air and she has a go*. No success. The next two hours are a bit of a blur. I have to have a general anaesthetic. It is very sad that my main thoughts at this time are not of our baby but of the placenta. I am obviously not allowed a drink. Quite a few doctors appear to discuss various things. A young doctor comes in to put in a drip. She has one go at inserting a wide needle with a hole in it in my hand, it is very painful, it doesn't work. She offers me a local anaesthetic before the next one. She has seven more goes and still no success. I have puncture marks all over my hands and lower arms. I am fighting back the tears. She eventually gives up and says that the anaesthetist will have a go in the pre-med room. The anaesthetist comes to see me first. She is very nice and inspires me with the confidence that she could get the drip in. In the pre-med room they admired my wounds inflicted by the previous doctor. They are also delighted to see me in the morning because I was on their list for a section in the afternoon. This makes me feel a lot better as I realize what I could be going through. I wake up in the recovery room. Mark has been sitting in the delivery room with a sleeping Henry until the room is needed and then sits in the corridor. We are taken up to the ward. I am drowsy after the anaesthetic and have to sit with a drip for the next three or four hours.

In retrospect, I was delighted with the labour and birth – it was exactly what I would have planned. I was really pleased that the breathing worked and that all the preparation was worth while. It was a shame about the messing about with the placenta. We never really got the chance to sit back and feel pleased. Apart from the drip it was just a minor hassle compared to the Caesarian section I would have had four hours later. Henry was just under 6 lb and very skinny although of average length. The next bit was the worst for me. As his temperature

* If the placenta is reluctant to emerge, sometimes the midwife may ease it out by pulling gently on the umbilical cord. Since this can be uncomfortable for the mother, it is useful to breathe some gas and air.

and blood sugar were low he went on to three-hourly blood tests for the next five days. I found this physically and emotionally exhausting. The midwives were excellent but I only felt he was mine when I got home.

What about the cases where not one, but two babies have to negotiate their way into the world. Anabel and David were very keen that Anabel should give birth to their twins naturally, and were desperate for the labour process to begin . . .

ANNABEL AND DAVID

'I was stunned and relieved that I had two healthy babies'

Amazingly, the twins had stayed inside me beyond 40 weeks, and medical heads were shaking and nodding, murmuring the words 'date for induction'. We hated the idea of my labour being started off artificially after what had been a healthy and happy pregnancy. We begged to be given a few more days to see if I could go into labour naturally, especially as there were no signs of placental insufficiency, blood group incompatibility, rising blood pressure or fetal distress. After several battles, three more days were granted, but I still did not go into labour naturally at home as I had hoped.

So, three days later we turned up at 8 am and were directed to the twins and breeches delivery room – a double delivery room full of hi-tech equipment, but with no place to put a vase of flowers or contemplate rolling around on cushions. There in the room was Sister X, thrilled at her first chance in years to deliver twins (both twins were head down so a midwife delivery seemed likely). She directed me to the bed, told David where to put our cases, pointed him to the chair, told me to take off my earrings and wedding ring, set about taking blood pressure, and told us what would happen.

For some women she may have been the kind of midwife to inspire confidence but for us – with her clear intention to manage the birth of our twins for us, and get them delivered before the end of her shift using 'jungle juice' (a form of oxytocin called Syntocinon) fed to me on a drip which produces much sharper contractions that all but necessitate an epidural – after nine months of thinking about how we wanted our birth to be, we were not going to have the choice taken from us like this.

Then arrived the senior registrar, two other doctors, and an anaesthetist, to look me over and tell us again what would happen. They admitted they could start the induction with a prostaglandin pessary instead of a drip, but it would take much longer and it might not get me into labour so the drip could still be needed and anyway I would have to have a drip put in in case things went wrong with my contractions for the second twin, or I had a post-partum haemorrhage, and I really should keep an open mind about the epidural. They left clearly thinking we were trouble-makers. Later, the senior registrar came back without the rest, to put the pessary in. He told us it should take six hours, but if things had not happened by then he could put in another pessary, but at least the labour would be more natural, and once the pessaries had got me to 3–4 cm dilated, then he could break my waters and things would definitely start happening.

That all sounded fine to us, so in went the pessary, and as we could not occupy the twins and breeches room for six hours or more until I had properly gone into labour, off we went back to the antenatal ward to have the twins' heartbeats monitored hourly, and to await the effect of the pessary. What a relief to have escaped the clutches of Sister X without further confrontation.

Then followed four pleasant hours, from 10 am to 2 pm, of feeling my first contractions without too much pain, reading, chatting to David and to the very friendly midwives who were so supportive, and keen that it should be us to make the choices. Then started much swifter and more painful contractions penetrating the back and front around my pelvis. 'OK!' I thought, 'I must be nearly 4 cm and the senior registrar will come and break my waters and then things can get going'. In came the consultant and senior registrar. I was examined and to our horror, despite all the pain I was only 1–2 cm dilated. The consultant said if nothing more had happened after the second pessary had gone in, I should be sent home for the weekend (in such agony?), and then he would deliver them himself on the Monday afternoon using induction from the Syntocinon drip. Out went the obstetricians, and the contractions got more and more unbearable.

I'm afraid I tensed up and lost my breathing; massage and yoga exercises seemed to make no difference, whatever I did; leaning forward, on all fours, squatting or hip rocking. I started to realize that if this was what 2 cm was like, I was not going to get through without an epidural. I asked them to call the senior registrar who arranged for us to be taken back down to the twins delivery room for an epidural as soon as possible. The contractions really were violent now, right into my back and anus, I panted through them while the saline drip and epidural were inserted, and what bliss when their excruciating effect started to wear off as the epidural anaesthetized them. I started to feel them only as back tightenings and then I relaxed, chatted to the two delightful midwives who had come to deliver me, and the senior registrar as he reassured me – I was 8 cm dilated now. He broke the waters, told me I had a pelvis like a bucket and stood a good chance of a midwife delivery – 'Much better for you and your perineum if it is', he said. (His own wife is four months pregnant, and they want a natural birth!)

I'm told it only took an hour between having the waters of the first twin broken, and reaching 10 cm and starting to push her out. The midwives and David directed me, in the pushing they supported my bent legs. I had no idea the pushing would be such hard work, and I was not in the best position with the epidural so I needed all the encouragement and morale boosting the three of them gave me. David was given various things to do and was totally involved in the birth. Eventually out came Ruth without my perineum tearing, twin one, with a head of long dark hair, presented punk style (I had been convinced she was a boy whilst she had been inside).

Once cleaned up, Ruth was given to David to hold whilst they set about helping the second twin to emerge. We knew it was head down, but my contractions had slowed down whilst pushing Ruth out, and Syntocinon ('jungle juice') had to be fed to me via the drip. The next problem was that once the waters of the second twin were broken, it did not seem to be head down any more, so the senior registrar had to put his hands inside and find its feet, swivel it around and prepare the way for a breech delivery with the help of forceps on the head at the end. 'Mind that perineum', said the midwife. He handed her the forceps and said, 'You mind it!', and that she did, carefully guiding out the head of Michael so as not to tear me. (I had been convinced that the twin that side was a girl!) He needed a little reviving after such a complicated birth, but eventually made a few noises and cried a little.

Once the placenta had been delivered, both twins were presented to me to suckle for a few minutes. Then up the three of us went to the post-natal ward to recover. I felt stunned and relieved that I had two healthy babies, but it took a couple of days before the enormity of what we had all achieved really hit me, and waves of passion for our two gorgeous babies surged within me. I still feel them (the twins are four days old as I write this), I hope I always will.

But I want to say that if I had not had that epidural (chosen because I could not ride the pain) that enabled the breech delivery, and the drip fitted (forced upon me – contrary to my hopes of being able to move around – to enable the contractions for Michael's birth), little Michael could have been brain damaged. I have learned that however normal or healthy the pregnancy with twins may be, and even if the twins' presentation is head down, the risks of the second twin turning into a difficult position are always there. It would be a great risk to go into a twin birth without either an epidural or a saline drip which if contractions stop, can be used to induce them with the hormone to ensure the second twin will be safely delivered vaginally.

I envy those who had a natural birth without epidural and were able to push their babies out in their best positions. But with twins, better a hi-tech birth of two healthy babies than one actively born and the other damaged.

Many doctors and midwives would agree with Anabel's categorical view, but many would not. If you are expecting twins and want to look into the options for delivery, talk with both your midwife and the doctor you see in hospital. The way the babies are lying, the size of your pelvis, your own and the babies' health, and the experience and views of the staff available, as well as whether you have given birth before, will all be factors in coming to the best possible choices for the birth.

7
Caesarian and Water Births

Sometimes a baby is not able to get out into the world through the vagina at all, or it is considered dangerous to let it try. This may be assessed and decided beforehand, and a Caesarian operation planned, or a crisis may happen during labour itself necessitating an emergency operation. The mother can, in the case of a planned Caesarian, choose between a general anaesthetic, which will make her unconscious during the operation and an epidural anaesthetic, which will completely anaesthetize her only below the waist so that she will be conscious to receive the baby as soon as it is delivered. If it is an *emergency* Caesarian a general anaesthetic has to be given because there is not time to insert and check an epidural.

During the operation a cut is made horizontally just above the pubic hair in the mother's abdomen, into the uterus, and the baby is lifted out through this route. Caesarian-born babies may need more 'sucking out' than their vaginally-born brothers and sisters because they do not get the squeeze down through the vagina which helps to push mucus out of their noses amd mouths.

In an emergency, a baby can be lifted out through the mother's abdomen within three to four minutes of arriving in the operating theatre. In these cases it is a dramatic and life-saving procedure.

Fear of litigation, particularly in the USA, has pushed the Caesarian rate up to almost 25 per cent in some hospitals. Once again, fierce debate continues about what exactly the criteria are for choosing Caesarian section as the best way to deliver any particular baby.

Let us start with Alison, who, a midwife herself, was quite sure that a Caesarian was the safest and most responsible choice for her baby's delivery, since the baby was breech, she was a 'primip' – i.e., a first-time mother, and the other signs were not favourable either. Because she was staying away from home with a friend, it happened that her operation was done in a hospital other than her local one . . .

ALISON

'Quite calm as I knew this was the day'

In the morning was my routine antenatal visit to the consultant at the health centre at 37 weeks, where he confirmed breech, even after attempting to move the baby round three times (and painfully) the week before. My pelvis appeared narrow, and the baby's bottom had not engaged at all into my pelvis. He arranged an X-ray for the next day, a mere formality. I was quite depressed – all my great plans out the window. He was a good obstetrician, knew his staff, but his manner was awkward and he preferred doing classical skin incisions (from belly button to pubic bone)* instead of the bikini-line cut; and he preferred using a general anaesthetic to epidural.

Edward met me, under a black cloud. He drove me to meet a friend to go shopping for my last-minute things for baby and hospital admission, when I felt my knickers very wet. I thought, well my bladder's not that weak, and the baby's not bouncing on it, so I guess my membranes have ruptured. We arrived half an hour later at her house, with a gush down to my knees of clear fluid with egg-white-like bits in. Phoned the local hospital just up the hill, then had a cheese sandwich and washed my hair, quite calm now as I knew this was the day!

My contractions were irregular, about every five to 10 minutes and getting a bit stronger, so that I had to pause to concentrate on my breathing. My friend lent me bits and clean clothes and then we went to the labour ward.

They were very pleasant on admission. I changed into a gown, and the consultant on call came and did a vaginal examination – it felt like up to his elbow. He said I was 3–4 cm, and could be transferred to my original consultant's hospital. I said 'Could I possibly stay here please?' and asked for an epidural. As the anaesthetist had to come in from the general hospital a mile away (no epidurals on demand in this part of Scotland!) they said they'd check with him first. Amazingly, yes, he was immediately available, new to the area, and very keen on epidurals.

So the rigmarole started: a thorough pubic shave, questions and more questions, and a massive needle in my arm for the intravenous fluid – after taking blood from the other arm for cross-matching. Trundled off to theatre – was the only time I got to see Edward, briefly

* This is quite rare these days.

in the corridor. The contractions were about every four minutes and a lot stronger and longer. The anaesthetist stopped when the pain took over, and the theatre sister/midwife helped me with my breathing. The relief at the end of the contraction was indescribable. I wasn't coping as well as I'd imagined, partly because I wasn't psyched up properly, and partly because I knew it wouldn't last for long.

The epidural I hardly noticed going in – only the slight stinging of the local anaesthetic, that was it. Then progressively my legs numbed, became hot, heavy and slightly 'buzzy' – really quite pleasant, and I was giggling whenever I tried to move. And no pain! It was obvious they weren't used to epidurals, as they didn't have things immediately to hand as they do in the hospital I work in – they said 'Oh yes we had one about two weeks ago!' at least the guy putting it in knew what he was doing, and kept chatting pleasantly the whole time.

In to the theatre, with a good audience, they started cutting (bikini line, thank goodness!). Because I'm a midwife, and was trying to peer over the screens, they took the green towel down, and I saw my little boy being lifted out – I could only vaguely feel rummagings, and I felt quite detached from it all, almost like it was someone else's body. He started crying vigorously as they cleared his airways, and I watched them check him over, with the tears pouring down my cheeks – the emotion of it all overwhelming me. The anaesthetist gave me his hanky! A minute later, he was wrapped in a towel and planted on my chest, instant silence from him, at my warmth and heartbeat.

So that was my experience. At least I experienced some labour, and reached 5 cm, and was conscious at his arrival into the world. I can recommend an epidural if it is necessary, and the exercises helped tremendously postnatally. A month later, Ewan is gaining weight well, is a contented baby, and I'm almost back to normal clothes and fitness. Breastfeeding is going very well.

Catriona was also a 'primip breech' – first-time mother and baby lying bottom down rather than head down. Catriona is a doctor and was also very concerned about the safety of her baby, but very much wanted a vaginal birth. We meet her first in the 38th week of her pregnancy, becoming as absent-minded as many of us do by that stage.

CATRIONA

'The entire world ran into the room'

Before I begin, let me just stress that it is all well worth it!

At 38 weeks the baby was still a breech presentation, headbutting me in the ribs and feet kicking me in the bladder! I had my antenatal appointment on the Monday morning with the consultant to see if I would be allowed to attempt a vaginal delivery. He had already offered me an elective Caesarian but I had refused. The week before I had had pelvic X-rays and an ultrasound of the baby's head to see if it would fit through. The baby was of average size and I had a pelvis 'like a bucket'! So I was to be allowed to attempt a vaginal delivery as long as I made – quote: 'absolutely normal progress' – written all over my notes.

Whoopee! I came away from the antenatal appointment with my head in the clouds. I *was* going to do it, despite everyone putting me off. That afternoon I managed to lock my car with the house keys inside on double yellow lines in the middle of the city centre in the heat of the sun. Oh good grief! I also had a nursing bra fitting session with the local NCT bra fitter – she suggested I had left it a bit too near the date, but I was convinced I was going to be late. She said that women usually followed the pattern of their mothers – mine had us three one month, two weeks and three weeks early.

That evening, mowing the lawn, I felt little niggles like period pains low down in my abdomen. At about 7 pm, off to the pub and they started getting a little stronger and more regular – every 25 minutes. Must be a practise run, I thought to myself, but insisted that my partner, Deepak, restrict himself to two pints of beer, just in case! By the end of the evening the contractions were coming every 20 minutes and distinctly putting me off my conversation and orange juice.

Home promptly as I desperately needed to cut my toe nails, thinking that I couldn't go into hospital with uncut toe nails. That put the contractions off for an hour, so we went to bed. Deepak told me to wake him if they became unbearable.

By 1 am they were coming every 10 minutes, and by 1.30 am every five minutes. Up we got, cursing that we were losing out on a night's sleep and taking it all a little more seriously.

Luckily I had packed my case the day before, so while I had a shower and washed my hair, Deepak got a few things ready and made me a cup of tea – which made me feel sick.

At 3 am we were off down the motorway with me screaming 'Slow down' around the corners, and 'Faster, faster!' on the straight bits. We arrived there at 3.30 am with the contractions seeming to come every few minutes. We were popped into a room with a low bed bringing with us bean bag and ghetto blaster. Somehow, I ended up in a hospital gown, open at the back, which had been one of those things that previously I had not wanted. But I was past caring, and the midwife seemed so insistent; next time no hospital gown. In the situation of having contractions every few minutes I lost all my usual assertiveness.

At 4 am my first vaginal examination. Up until then I had managed to cope well with the contractions by leaning against the wall and wiggling my hips with the deep abdominal breathing practised so much in my antenatal classes. The surprising thing was how quickly the contractions came on – no time to take up position and get into the rhythm of breathing, so each time I had to be well prepared.

For the vaginal examination I had to be on the bed, of course, and this made coping with the contractions impossible. At 4 am I was 3 cm dilated – 7 cm to go! By 4.30 am I was having an enormous urge to push, which I thought was a bit odd. The midwife explained that this comes a lot earlier with breeches because the bottom can start slipping through way before the cervix is fully dilated and then the head can get stuck. For this reason they recommended I have an epidural. At 5 am we made the decision to have one.

The hardest thing, again, is the lying still while having the epidural. The contractions were coming like waves and I was trying to breathe my way through them. That was definitely one of the hardest times and the epidural seemed to take forever.

Unfortunately, it didn't work, or at least, it did a bit, on the left side, but I could still feel the contractions on the right and still had an incredible urge to push.

At 8 am I had my next examination – 9 cm dilated! Whoopee! We were overjoyed. The consultant came in and cheered us on. The midwife fixed a fetal heart monitor on the baby's bottom. Then left us alone with a student midwife, the monitor showed a slowing of the baby's heart rate down to 70 after a contraction. She immediately hit the alarm bell and it seemed like the entire world ran into the room. I was whisked onto my side and given an oxygen mask. It was all very frightening. After a few more of these, and finally one where the heart rate dropped to 60 during a contraction, we were taken around to the delivery room, all the while trying not to push. It felt like the baby was almost dropping out, so near!

DIn the delivery room I had another examination – fully dilated, but then her heart rate dropped to 50. The registrar shouted: 'Caesarean, no preparation!' and we were whisked out to the lifts and up to the theatres. At this point I didn't dare look at Deepak, I felt so disappointed and shocked. Everything had been going so well, and now the baby was at risk.

We arrived at the theatre and everything happened so quickly – I had to have a general anaesthetic, and my last memory was Deepak with tears streaming down his face. The baby was out within three minutes, and by this time her heart rate was down to 20 and everyone thought she was going to be 'flat'.* But good old Florence let out an enormous cry as she was lifted out and was perfect. The umbilical cord was around her neck and under her arm, so every time she came down with a contraction she compressed the cord and cut off her own blood supply.

I woke up from the anaesthetic to see Florence – 6 lb 10 oz – and then passed out again. Luckily Deepak was there to be with her and bath her. Unfortunately she was so zonked from the anaesthetic she didn't feed for 12 hours.

That day was very odd. Mixed feelings of elation, disappointment, pain! In fact, the entire week in hospital was incredibly emotional and difficult at times. A word of advice – if a Caesarian might be on the cards, take in some big 'granny knickers'!

It's now five weeks on and the scar still hurts a little, but the horrible memories of the frightening moments are fading, and Florence is wonderful!

Do not underestimate what you and your body have gone through if you have had a Caesarian. Rest as much as you can to help your body to heal and do not hurry to get 'back to normal'. You have had an operation and a major life upheaval all at once.

Almost at the other extreme are labours which take place in the water. The soothing effects of the warm water of a birthing pool, and the relative weightlessness for the heavy, pregnant body of being water-borne, enable many labouring women to delay the use of analgesic drugs or forego them altogether. The presence of the water itself seems to calm the atmosphere: 'We have . . . noticed how midwives often speak in quieter tones and move more gently when in the pool room'.

* This is medical vernacular to describe a baby who is born limp and unresponsive, and needs vigorous resuscitation to get it breathing.

(Burns and Greenish, 'Pooling Information', *Nursing Times* Vol. 89, No. 8, 1993)

Warm water seems to be of valuable assistance in handling pain. More controversial are three other factors. First, initial though very small-scale studies show that perineal tears in women who actually push their babies out into the water are more frequent than in women who give birth out of water. Second, although many babies are born safely into the water and breathe spontaneously only on surfacing into the air, there is concern about this in some obstetric quarters and an urgent need for more collection and analysis of data. Third, if a baby is born in the water, even practitioners, who never ever intervene in the woman's own spontaneous behaviour if they can help it, tend to move women out of the pool before the placenta detaches, to guard against the risk of water embolism.* In contrast to this some practitioners do not feel delivery in the water poses any risk and are in no hurry to move women out of the water for the third stage.

Giving birth in the water is not well researched and documented yet, so we await a sufficient body of evidence on most of these issues. In the meantime, practitioners work as always on the balance of maximum safety and maximum creativity and suitability of care.

Melanie and Frank had organized a birthing pool in their house for the birth of their first child . . .

MELANIE

'I felt I had my own private haven'

I went to bed at 10 pm on Monday with mild contractions thinking they would ease off in the night. However, we got up again at 11 pm as I couldn't sleep and the contractions were getting closer together. I didn't really believe that anything significant was going to happen but thought that Frank was taking it seriously, getting dressed and setting a fire in the lounge.

The midwife arrived just after midnight and confirmed that I was in labour and my cervix 2 cm dilated. I was so pleased that things were progressing with what seemed like hardly any effort. The contractions felt like period pains and I was most comfortable walking around

* A water embolism is a small quantity of water entering the mother's circulation – which could be fatal.

between the lounge and the kitchen. I timed my walking to coincide with the contractions and between them I told Frank and the midwife how I wanted the birth pool organized and went over our birth plan. Once the rooms had been organized we decided to watch a video, and I alternated between the sofa and the kitchen, pacing the floor during contractions. At 4.30 am I was 5 cm dilated and starting to find breathing and walking difficult. I was getting out of breath and finding contractions very uncomfortable, and I felt that now was the right time to get into the pool; I had wanted to wait before getting in until I was no longer comfortable just walking around. I needed to know I had an alternative method of dealing with contractions. Frank had filled the pool earlier! This took an hour and now he checked that it was still at body temperature. A second midwife arrived because of the pool and the home birth. I got into the pool at 5 am and immediately felt that all the uncomfortable sensations had been taken away. It was fantastic and I asked the midwife if the contractions had stopped. They obviously hadn't as when I got out 15 minutes later for a pee, it was very uncomfortable being out of the water. My pulse went down a lot in the water and went up again whenever I got out. I felt I could breathe properly again as I was so relaxed. And it was great not having to carry my weight around, and to be able to float freely in the water. The water seemed very warm, which it had to be should the baby be born in it, and I kept getting thirsty. Frank kept putting drinks on a floating tray in the pool and between contractions I felt that I was in a jacuzzi chatting to and laughing with friends. The pool was in our study which is small and cosy, and with the curtains drawn and being lit by candlelight I felt incredibly cosy and safe inside it. I felt that I had my own private haven to sink into and the midwives left Frank and I alone in the study a lot of the time.

For the first hour of being in the pool I was barely aware of contractions, whilst during the second hour they gradually intensified as time went on. I moved my body around in the water during contractions and 'drew' shapes with my body to focus my attention away from the discomfort. I got out of the pool every 15 minutes or so to go to the toilet and during these times I was acutely aware of the pain of the contractions – it was such a different experience being in the water.

I would dash back in as soon as I could and feel so relieved on getting into the water. In the water I felt completely in control. Towards the end of two hours in the pool I moved into transition. I felt very scared and overwhelmed by this and clutched Frank during contractions which were now coming in continuous waves. This seemed to last for about 20 minutes. Until now the whole experience of labour had been very pleasurable but now I felt frightened and concerned that this feeling would get worse.

I was still in the pool and the midwives asked Frank and I to decide where we wanted our baby to be born, in the water or on the floor. I felt completely undecided; it seemed that if I got out of the pool contractions would be unbearable yet I didn't feel sure about the baby emerging into water. We discussed it for a few minutes and decided that I would try getting out, as we had planned to do this, and I would give birth in the lounge, but that I would go back into the water if I found it too unpleasant to be out. As soon as I stepped out of the pool I got a tremendous urge to push and felt I needed to be on solid ground I ran into the lounge and got onto all fours on the mattress on the floor. I put my head and hands forward onto the sofa in front and didn't want to move anymore. I felt very much in control and breathed with my mouth open as the contractions came. I had regular and frequent urges to push which were overwhelming and shocking. The midwife examined me and could feel the baby's head in my vagina. When she told me this I couldn't really believe it; even when Frank said he could see the head it just didn't sink in. It was when the midwife asked Frank to get clothes for the baby that it suddenly hit me.

There was going to be a baby and I was going to have to push him or her out. I found the pushing incredibly painful, I didn't want to have any form of chemical pain relief but I knew that if I worked with it I would have the baby I had waited so many months for. I found that I could control the pushing and knew that if I didn't work with it, things might take a long time so eventually nearly one and a half hours after pushing started I pushed Bridget's head out, and a few minutes later her body. I felt enormous relief as I felt her slide out and then heard her little cries. I thought: 'Great, I've done it'.

I flopped onto my stomach on the cushion in front and heard Frank saying: 'It's a girl' and sobbing at the same time. I then turned round and Frank handed me our gorgeous baby daughter, Bridget. It was 8.30 in the morning and what a morning it was!

Joanna had her first baby in the UK and her second in Australia. Here is her account of the second baby's arrival . . .

JOANNA

'I just floated in the water'

Wednesday 25 January
Woke up with a very tight bearing down sensation in my tummy which persisted even after I had got up and pottered around the house for a while. I decided to think nothing of it due to the fact that exactly the same thing had happened three weeks earlier and had lasted most of the day – only to find that everything had (rather disappointingly) returned to normal by the evening, by which time everyone was in a state of anticlimax. We had planned this second birth so happily and with so much eager anticipation. The birth of my first child (now 18 months old) was, not to put too fine a point on it, a bitter disappointment – a catalogue of every single thing I *didn't* want to happen and so this second birth was to be different. In the particular part of the country (Australia) where we live there is a lot of participation in and support for home birth and so, with the blessings and good wishes of my doctor, this is what we had planned, although I was totally prepared for a hospital transfer should it become necessary. I had two midwives who worked as a team and who I had got to know through several home visits prior to the birth. We had become close, like friends and I felt totally confident and secure about the birth. Anyway, to return to Wednesday morning, the tight heavy feeling continued in my lower tummy all day, rather like a period pain but with a heavy feeling around my cervix. We went shopping, determined as I was to ignore the sensation, convinced it was yet again another false alarm as I still had a week to go to full term.

By 8 pm that evening I was beginning to think that I might be having contractions but I was still unsure as there was no pain, no show and no leaking fluid from my membranes, as there had been with my first birth. I rang my midwife and told her what was happening and just told her that I could be ringing again that night! She told me she would ring me in one hour. At 9 pm I was starting to think that maybe the tightening feelings were beginning to pick up a bit and take on some sort of regularity. Jenny, my midwife, rang again and said they were leaving at about 10 pm and would be here in one hour. By 10 pm I had got onto the bed on all fours and was breathing through my contractions which my husband had been timing – five minutes apart, then by 10.15 pm, three minutes apart. I asked Leo (my husband) to fill up the bath – it was quite a hot night but I was starting to get the shivers a little. At 10.30 pm I climbed into the bath, by which time I was starting to concentrate on my contractions, which were not intense, but I couldn't exactly ignore them either! As soon as I was in the bath, the most incredible thing happened. The contractions seemed *so* much less painful. I just floated in the water, resting my head on the back of the bath. I was able to totally relax my whole body and I no longer had to worry about getting into a comfortable position to handle the contractions. It was as if my whole body seemed to become weightless and the only thing that I could feel was my tummy, which looking back on it was a good thing as I was able to completely relax and go with the contractions. At 11 pm Jenny and Leslie arrived. They quickly brought candles into the bathroom and switched off the bright lights. I felt *so* relaxed, confident and in control of the situation. I could hardly believe it was happening. Here I was in full labour (in the bath!) and almost enjoying it! I felt no fear, just inner calm and confidence. I knew now that I would just go with it and simply allow my body to give birth as Nature had always intended. By 11.30-ish the contractions were becoming more intense, and were coming every minute, even less, 45 seconds. My whole body started to tingle, as if I had pins and needles. The sensation became very intense and the voices started to become distant. I heard Jenny say that a lot of women went off on a sort of high during transition – almost as if they were on a drug, which was exactly how I felt: as if someone had given me a shot of morphine. It really was the most remarkable feeling. I knew I was in transition now and I couldn't believe how well I was handling it – piece of cake compared to the first time I thought to myself and gave myself a pat on the back! I could actually feel my whole pelvis starting to open up, as if my cervix was being pushed open from the inside, and then the familiar pushing sensation in my bottom – I knew I was close. Then with the next contraction, my body gave its first involuntary big push and then I knew the baby would be born soon. After three big pushes, with that sensation of wanting to pass a football through my back passage(!), I felt the baby coming down. Then it really started to hurt and I knew I had to do this quickly. Jenny said she could see her head and there was a lot of excited chatter going on. All I wanted was to get it over with by then. I decided not to wait for the contractions before I pushed and just got on with pushing anyway! Two or three pushes and her head was born – two more and her whole body was born at 12.15 Thursday morning. Jenny lifted her gently through the water onto my tummy and chest. She started breathing instantly and just lay there making little grunting noises. We all sobbed – them with joy and emotion, and me with relief and a whole mixture of other things I couldn't begin to identify! We lay there for half an hour before Jenny cut the cord.

It was all so perfect. We named her Megan Louise. She weighed 7 lb exactly. She had dark brown hair with a few little curls on top. As soon as I got into bed – having pushed out the placenta in the bath – she suckled from my breast for 20 minutes and then fell asleep until dawn between Leo and I. I fell asleep feeling so fulfilled.

She's now one month old and I still can't believe this happened to me. I never planned an underwater birth but if I ever have another baby, I wouldn't consider doing it any other way. Jenny says it was the easiest and most natural birth she has ever attended. I didn't even tear my perineum, which suffered an extremely large cut during my first birth, so the discomfort afterwards was minimal.

I just feel so happy that I was able to experience this birth, which was a catalogue of everything I *did* want to happen, and I sincerely hope that every woman has a chance to have the kind of birth that she hopes for, whatever it may be, at least once.

8
Breathing, Exercises and a Few Final Words

Breathing

Here are the breathing techniques and exercises to which the women refer as they tell their stories.

Handling contractions

Steady 'yoga' breathing is the most useful for getting through contractions. First of all, when you are in the first stage of labour, do not do any special form of breathing until you need to. If you do yoga breathing from your first twinge you will be absolutely exhausted by the time you are 4 cm dilated! Remember how many of the women whose birth stories we have read managed by 'saving up' different options for when the going got tough.

While you can, then, just 'watch' your contractions come and go, as dull, period-pain-like aches which wax and wane. They will steadily build in intensity. As soon as they make you want to wince, or gasp, or screw your face up, you have reached the point where it is useful to 'change gear' and slide into your yoga-style breathing. Practise it during the pregnancy and you will be able to do it without conscious effort when the time comes.

1. Sit tall out of your hips. Relax your shoulders and lengthen the back of your neck. Relax your hips, knees, hands, and feet. Feel your spine is long.

2. Start breathing a little more deeply and a little more slowly than usual. Hear the breath as it comes and goes. Rest one hand lightly on your lower abdomen.

3. When the rhythm of your breathing is settled, start to breathe in through your nose, and out through your mouth. Do not blow the breath out. Part your lips and let the air escape.

4. Become aware of the hand on your abdomen. As you breathe in, send the breath down to your hand. You are filling up so your abdomen swells a little. Exhale as if from the area under your

hand. You are emptying so your abdomen subsides a little. Continue in your own rhythm.

5. After a few minutes of this, gently remove your hand from your abdomen. Let your breathing return to an everyday level. If your eyes are closed, blink them open gently while you get used to the light. Do not rush around, take a few moments to reorientate yourself before you return to the activities of the day.

Notice how calm and pleasant you feel after even a few minutes of this. This form of breathing is unlikely to make you feel *serene* during labour (a few women do, but not very many) but it does make you feel more calm, and does help to ride the pain. Because you do not fight the pain and tense up, the contractions can be that much more effective in opening the cervix too.

Practise this breathing until you can go straight to stage 4 with no preamble, in any position, and without a hand on your abdomen to check whether you are doing it correctly or not. Once you have developed the skill that far, you will be able to use it in labour. Furthermore, you will find you automatically use it any time you are in pain or under stress (or both!) and that it is an invaluable addition to your repertoire of coping mechanisms.

Useful positions for first stage

While just breathing is enough to get you through your contractions, use it on its own. You will probably get to a point where even though you are breathing steadily and deeply you are starting to tense up, grimace, or want to cry. When that happens a simple change of position can be invaluable. Try any of these which feel right.

1. Stand facing the wall, about a foot away from it, feet hip-distance apart. Fold your arms and rest them on the wall, rest your head on your arms. Let your knees 'give' a little.

   Move smoothly into your deep abdominal breathing. Sway your hips. Experiment with what suits you. Try side-to-side, backwards and forwards, figures of eight. Keep your whole pelvis relaxed. This position is helpful in early first stage when breathing alone is no longer enough.

2. As labour progresses you may find you want to 'get down to it' more. Try all fours, on the floor or on the bed. Do your deep, slow breathing and rock and sway your hips. When you practise

antenatally, try different hip movements to see what suits you. In labour, your body will probably prompt you instinctively as to what to do. If you are very tired, instead of all fours, you may want to kneel with your knees hip-distance apart and flop forwards onto a bean bag or a pile of cushions. Try to relax your whole pelvis, remember that everything needs to stretch and open up.

3. Squatting with knees wide apart and resting your arms around the shoulder of a helper on either side may be useful too. Breathe slowly as you have practised and allow your hips to shift around naturally.

Remember that these are just suggestions. There is no formal, set 'technique'. Cast your mind back over the birth stories and the many different positions which women adopted spontaneously to help themselves. Breathe slowly and deeply, get your awareness out of your intellect and down into your hips, and you will know what is right for you.

Waiting for an anterior 'lip' to clear

You will have noticed in several of the birth stories that it was sometimes necessary to resist the urge to push while a last 'lip' of cervix dilates. A useful breathing pattern in this predicament is:

1. Relax shoulders, relax pelvic area, inhale slowly and deeply.
2. Exhale in a rapid repeated pattern of 'puff, puff, blow', until all the breath is exhaled.

Repeat while the contraction lasts. In between contractions, breathe normally and relax as much as you can.

Practise your 'huff, huff, blow' pattern so that it is familiar and available if you need it.

Panting while the baby's head is born

It is beneficial both for you and your baby if the baby's head eases out slowly rather than bursting out! In particular, controlling your breathing at this stage can be the greatest help in avoiding a perineal tear. Pushing your baby down to the entrance of your vagina, as you can see from all the different accounts, can take anything from one big push to an hour-and-a-half of powerful pushes.

When we see a new baby we all say: 'Oh, isn't it tiny!', but at this stage in labour the baby, however tiny, feels very big indeed. The pressure you feel is all in the back passage and it does indeed feel as though the baby is intending to make its exit there rather than through your vagina. Do not panic – it will not! Simply think of bulging your whole perineum out in as relaxed a way as you can.

When the baby's head is about to emerge the midwife will ask you to 'Pant, not push'. Relax your face, particularly your mouth, and pant lightly and rapidly. Bulge and relax your perineum. As the largest part of the head comes through you will feel an intense burning stretching, and probably a sense of the impossibility of it all. To get an idea of what the physical sensation is like, stretch your mouth wide open with your fingers. Notice how intense the stretching sensation is, although you are not damaging your mouth at all. The birth of the baby's head creates a similar sensation in your vagina.

Alternating between pushing and panting as the shoulders emerge can also be significant in avoiding damage to your perineum and in allowing your baby to squeeze out gently rather than being catapaulted out! Listen to your midwife and follow what she says. To practise beforehand, imagine yourself at the last minutes of your labour, just about to give birth. Imagine yourself pushing powerfully, hearing your midwife saying 'Pant, now!' and change to light, rapid panting, mouth relaxed, perineum bulging warmly. Even when it starts to really sting and burn, keep panting lightly, with your mouth and perineum relaxed. You are nearly there! Now, imagine that your baby's head is born, and you hear your midwife saying something like this:

> 'Give a strong push now. Come on push, push, push! – and pant! Good, keep panting. Keep panting. Can you give a little push? – Great! pant again, keep panting for me, great, – and . . .'

Whoosh! At this point your baby is completely born.

It is quite emotional even to practise, isn't it? Become used to switching from pushing to panting smoothly and comfortably, and you will be familiar and ready with the process even during the high drama of late second stage labour.

Exercises

If you wish to remain fit during your pregnancy, go swimming, try antenatal yoga, or ordinary yoga class and inform the teacher that you are pregnant. If you are already well into an aerobic or running programme and have no history of miscarriage and no other problems with the pregnancy, continue with your programme but do tell your instructor or trainer that you are pregnant. Do not start on a vigorous new programme early on in a pregnancy, and do not do weight-training. You will be doing plenty of that naturally later on! Some pregnancy/exercise books are listed in Further Reading (at the back of the book).

General fitness is of great value during labour. Many of the uncomfortable feelings during the exertions of labour are familiar and therefore less frightening to women who train hard or play a vigorous sport. However, not every woman wants to be an athlete, pregnant or not, and nobody should feel under pressure to be one. A few very basic exercises will help increase flexibility around the back, hips, and thighs, and are of benefit even if you have no intention of pursuing any other fitness programme at all.

1. *Squatting* Squat for a few minutes each day. If your calves feel tight at first, squat with your heels on a thick book each to support them. If it is difficult to balance, have a few cushions or a low stool under your bottom to support you. Spread your knees wide and spread the whole perineal area. Relax your eyes, face, and shoulders, keep your back long and breathe steadily. Squatting really does help to make the perineum more stretchy, and this may make it less likely that you will need an episiotomy.
2. *Buddha Konasana* Sit on the floor with your spine tall, shoulders relaxed. Put the soles of your feet together, clasp them with your hands, and draw them towards you. Let your knees fall out to the sides. Eventually they will rest on the floor! Remain in this position breathing steadily, for a few minutes.
3. *Upavistha Konasana* Sit on the floor with your spine tall, shoulders relaxed. Spread your legs as wide apart as they will go. Breathe steadily and remain in this position for a few minutes. Next, on an exhalation, keeping your back flat, walk your hands forwards along the floor straight ahead of you. Go only as far as is right for you for today. Feel a good stretch, but no strain. Stay for 30 seconds, then walk your hands back towards you to come up. Move your legs back together slowly.

Just doing these three stretches for a few minutes most days will enhance your flexibility in the areas which matter most.

A few final words

Now that we have shared so many births so vividly, it seems fatuous to try to sum the experience of childbirth up in a neat and tidy way. It is simply a powerful experience that each of us, male or female, goes through once when being born ourselves, and then, if female, may have the opportunity to go through once or a handful of times in the other role, later on. If you are a man, you may have a chance to be there when your children are born. The pain, and the miracle, do not get any less, no matter how many times you encounter it or go through it. Because it is such a basic, primitive, and elemental experience, it brings to the surface all manner of other things. Love and a sense of wonder in the world may be renewed; new self-respect and pride, simply from having survived it, may develop.

The babies you have just read about are all at school now. Not all the partnerships that produced them have survived. The pressures of bringing up a family in these bewildering times is often too much even for a loving relationship to withstand. Reading through all the birth stories again gives me a strange sense of the city continually renewing itself. The pattern of births would ripple along certain streets, almost as if, as we often joked, pregnancy *was* a highly contagious condition.

The birth stories are shared here in the hopes that they are valuable to anyone focusing on birth in particular, whether as a parent, a midwife, a doctor or a health visitor; and also in the hopes that they are valuable to anyone in a life phase where they want to be *reborn*, make a new beginning, when it is useful to re-connect with the experience of childbirth itself for inspiration and energy.

We finish with one last baby, one last birth . . .

'Gazing at each other, waiting for dawn'

30 July

04.00 A dull backache and period-like pain awakens me for the second night running. I read a while, willing it to go away: my husband doesn't arrive from overseas until 1 August and the baby isn't due until the 12 August. Ache subsides but returns at hourly intervals.

07.00 I go to the loo and there is a show: I promptly burst into tears. Not today . . . please. But by 7.30 am I feel today's the day and feel a strange calm and resolve. I ask my mother to be my birth partner and feel very sad that my 'trained and psyched up' husband won't be there.

08.30 I'm having 30-second contractions every five minutes and I phone the hospital who tell me to come in. I give my mother a run-down on natural birth whilst I kneel in the back of the car and sway my hips as she rubs my lower back.

09.45 The first vaginal examination at 9.45 am reveals little progress: 1.5 cm dilated and the contractions remain roughly the same for most of the morning, increasing to 50 seconds every two or three minutes by 2 pm when I'm 3 cm dilated. This is going to be a long one. Midwife No. 2 comes on duty and by 6 pm I'm 5 cm dilated so we decide to break the waters as progress seems so slow. But I'm happy rocking and swaying and breathing. There is meconium in the waters and the midwife insists on a fetal scalp monitor. Blast. I worry that the labour will spiral downwards as I'm now tied to the bed. But I hang over the back and rock up and down, my mum breathing with me and saying, 'Relaaax!' I hear my antenatal teacher saying, 'Breathe in peace, breathe out tension'. I am amazed that I can still discuss pain relief options with the midwife (now No. 3, Penny) and remember insisting that I didn't need anything as I could still smile between contractions. Even when I was tempted, wondering when it would ever end, my main thought was if I take anything now it'll just take longer to recover and I knew that was the worse option.

22.00 Must be in transition. Huff, huff, blow and moan and groan. There's a lip and I mustn't push and I'm amazed at my body's expulsive pushes.

23.00 I try gas and air and only take it correctly once: yuk! I push it away as I can't concentrate on my breathing. Suddenly I'm being wheeled along corridors and round bends to the delivery room but still they say: 'Don't push as the baby isn't in the right position yet'. I'm still very confused about this but my mother tells me that one side of my belly was almost flat and the baby a big lump on the other side. At last I can push but I can't get comfortable: either for me or for the midwife. I start off on all fours, then try squatting but I'm virtually sitting on the baby's head, and Penny says she needs to see more of my perineum if we want to avoid an episiotomy or tear – especially as, she says, I'm so small. (In retrospect, I now think that if my husband had been there we could have tried a supported squat). I end up in the position I've always sworn I'd never give birth in: half lying, and in fact it did slow things down and helped avoid any damage. There seem to be lots of people watching and I'm given oxygen as the baby's heart rate is slow or is it fast? Confusion. I can push four or five times per contraction but only feel a real opening up during the first two. I remember watching myself lying gasping in the mirror at the end of the bed as the head inches forward, two steps forward, one back, black hair. But I can still recover between contractions, even now after 10 hours. Thank goodness for all that swimming. I feel in complete control panting and pushing. Yes, I can hold back, but when the head is born and Penny says: 'Come on Sweet-pea, push for the shoulders', I am amazed at the effort needed to get them out and it feels as if he suddenly shoots out of me and down the bed, a red and grey squiggle, crying loudly and I'm yelling too. I'm surprised that he doesn't look like ET! Only his hands and feet are wrinkled and there's very little vernix and little blood. He lies there looking about him, watchful.

Much later after we're both cleaned and tucked up in bed, we lie gazing at each other, waiting for dawn.

Further Reading

Barbara Dale and Joanna Roeber, *Exercises for Childbirth*. Century 1982.
Sophy Hoare, *Yoga and Pregnancy*. Unwin Paperbacks 1985.
Frédérick Leboyer, *The Art of Breathing*. Element Books 1985.
Deng Ming-Dao, *365 Tao: Daily Meditations*. HarperCollins 1992.
Paddy O'Brien, *Birth and Our Bodies*. Pandora Press 1988.
Paddy O'Brien, *Managing Two Careers: How to survive as a working mother*. Sheldon Press 1989.
Paddy O'Brien, *Your Life After Birth*. Pandora Press 1988.

Index